Wandering
Backwards

Wandering Backwards

MOLLY O'CONNOR

GSPH

GENERAL STORE PUBLISHING HOUSE
499 O'Brien Road, Box 415
Renfrew, Ontario, Canada K7V 4A6
Telephone (613) 432-7697 or 1-800-465-6072
www.gsph.com

ISBN 978-1-897508-51-0

Design and composition: Magdalene Carson / New Leaf Publication Design
Printed by Custom Printers of Renfrew Ltd., Renfrew, Ontario
Printed and bound in Canada

Library and Archives Canada Cataloguing in Publication

O'Connor, Molly
Wandering backwards / Molly O'Connor.
ISBN 978-1-897508-51-0
1. World War, 1939-1945--Canada--Fiction. I. Title.
PS8629.C653W35 2009   C813'.6   C2009-906264-X

CONTENTS

As I watch my grandchildren mature, I am fascinated with that transition from toddler to the young child who sees for the first time beyond his own space and reaches out to embrace it. It comes about subtly around seven or eight years into life when they can venture beyond the safety of a yard and a nurturing house and can shake off the supervision of an anxious adult to test life. They are touched by outside influences, led by caring parents, and form bonds with peers. I thought about my seventh year. It was a time of new happenings and discovery — a year to wander.

All the people and events in this book are real
except those that aren't.

MOTHER AND ME

FATHER

MY BROTHER, RAY

AUNT NELL

Memories on Bloomsgrove

Everyone, at some time, tries to recapture foregone days either to rid themselves of ghosts or perhaps to reclaim them. Some of us seek out images in family photo albums, recount childhood stories with a family member or chum, or, as I did, take a drive down the streets where we spent those days.

I stepped out of my dusty old Buick in front of #19 Bloomsgrove Avenue, and it was as if I were standing there, over sixty long years ago, when my family moved into this duplex.

1

JUNE 1944 — MOVING

Most of the homes on Bloomsgrove Avenue had verandas but ours at number 19 was the only one with a trumpet vine. It spread from the ground to the eaves, covered the entire driveway side, and reached partway around to the street side of the house, its broad leaves forming a sheltered hideaway. My brother, Ray, and I spent our first few days in our new home peering through that dense foliage and watching this strange new world. Sullenly, I scrunched tight into the corner remembering that fateful day only one week ago when I sat on another veranda many miles away.

All morning I sat on that veranda, huddled against the outside living room wall and tightly hugging Janice, my favourite doll, my chin buried in her blonde tresses. I watched three burly men wearing brown coveralls carrying my life, all seven years of it, in bits and pieces to a large moving van. I watched my bed being hauled away by arms wet with perspiration. They packed away my childhood and all the dreams my bed had witnessed. I prayed they would bring them back — my bed and my dreams. I watched the dining room furniture, our centre of family debate, complete with scratches and stains, disappear deep into the yawning cavern at the back of the truck. Our precious piano, draped and tugged by grunting men, uttered despairing notes as it, too, disappeared into that dark hole. My days on Duncan Street were being hauled away forever.

As we departed from Huntsville in our 1939 Ford coupe, I watched my home, my street, everything I knew disappear out the rear window as we turned the corner and headed for a place far away. I swallowed lumps and squinted hard to squeeze back the tears that threatened to tumble out from behind my eyelids. It was June 9, 1944. School was not yet out for the summer, but Ray and I had been granted early leave. I was passed out of Grade 1 and Ray Grade 4. When we turned that corner and our house disappeared behind an old oak tree, so did my best friend, Peter, waving in the distance. I had no friends where we were going.

My chin crushed the blonde curly hair of my ever-smiling Janice clasped close to my heart, and I sank deeper into the corner of the back seat. I knew it would not be long before I would be heaving up my breakfast in spite of the chain dragging from the tailpipe and the brown paper bag taped against my chest underneath my sundress. Last week, my mother tried yet another surefire remedy for carsickness and had me sucking on lemons. Nothing prevented the dizzy head and churning stomach I suffered every road trip. I stared at my black patent-leather shoes, now a size too small, and wiggled my toes just to enjoy the pain. Ray drew his long skinny legs to his chest and huddled in the other corner, partly because he was angry we were moving, but mostly to get as far away from me as possible before I upchucked.

We waited to merge onto the highway as rumbling trucks passed carrying logs from the vast hardwood forests that swept north through the Muskokas to the lumbermill in Huntsville. From blocks away you could hear the whine of the saws that left piles of sawdust crowning the shoreline of the Muskoka River. The town also had a tannery. Any breeze from the east had all the dogs lifting their noses to breathe in their scent of choice, and humans holding theirs to ward off the offensive odours of putrefied pulp and rotting hides. The truck drivers offloaded their cargoes and headed for the local hotels, staggering out hours later. My parents wanted a gentler life away from drunken lumberjacks and mill hands that were more often than not locked up overnight in the cells behind my father's office. "Drunken fools," father would mutter. My father had been chief of police in Huntsville for eleven years; now he would be the chief in Port Hope, a town in southern Ontario.

"Wave goodbye to Huntsville," my father cheerily called out as we drove under the stone arch that was the entrance to Huntsville. It said, "Welcome to Huntsville" on one side and "Come Again" on the other. None of us waved.

The brown paper rustling against my tummy or the chain rattling along the pavement must have helped, because I made it all the way to Gravenhurst before Dad had to stop the car on account of my heaving stomach. I made it to the ditch, much to Ray's relief. Mom wiped my face with the ever-ready damp cloth and gave me refreshing ice cubes to suck on, along with a sympathetic hug. Settled back in the car, we were off again.

Mom pointed out all the highlights along Highway 11: the lakes, the fields of dandelions, the granite rock cliffs. I managed to get all the way to a gas station at Sheppard Avenue on the outskirts of Toronto before heaving again. I don't know why Ray always cringed in the corner — I made it to the roadside every time, that's how good I was with the puking thing. Exhausted, I fell asleep somewhere along Sheppard Avenue and didn't wake until Dad announced we were in Port Hope. I stared at the strange new surroundings that would be home. We entered town through a canopy of leaves shading the main street, which wound down a steep hill. It was dusk, and soft shadows played over walls of large brick homes with gleaming white verandas lining the street. Huntsville had a few stone houses, but mostly there were wood frame houses because lumber was plentiful. I stared out at an alien world.

"Port Hope is famous for its magnificent chestnut and giant elm trees that heap shade on much of the town," Dad announced.

Ray and I had been told the town was perched high on bluffs overlooking Lake Ontario, with grand homes majestically watching the harbour, reminders of United Empire Loyalists who had settled and prospered in the area in the late 1700s. The Ganaraska River sliced through the town, entering from the north and heading toward the lake. It turned abruptly to twist behind Walton Street, the main street, heading east before it turned again and ran straight for the lake. The town swept upward away from the lake and the river like a three-sided bowl. Walton Street raced down Monkey Mountain, levelling out as it meandered beside the Ganaraska, then crossed it, turned south, and left town along the east shore of Lake Ontario. Every street in the heart of Port Hope climbed a hill or straddled the river, or both. Nearly all the residential streets were graced with homes of distinction that at one time commanded acreage, reminders of the town's early prosperity. Now the elegant, functional, and affordable were intermixed.

We pulled into the driveway of a modest, rusty-red brick duplex with a shared roof, wall and veranda; both sides had white trim. Our side needed paint. The front door opened into a hallway with a living room on the right, stairs going up on the left, and the kitchen straight ahead. The dining room was tucked in behind the living room and beside the kitchen. Upstairs there were three bedrooms. Mom and Dad had the biggest one, at the front of the house overlooking the street, Ray had the one at the back with a window that looked out on the roof of the garage and the backyard, and I was squeezed in the middle. My window looked at the neighbours' brick wall.

Now, a week later, Mom was busy unpacking and "getting us settled." Dad was off to learn all about the police station. Ray and I spent our time crouched behind the vines on the veranda, watching Bloomsgrove Avenue. People appeared and reappeared at regular times, doors opened, and dogs rushed out to lift their legs or squat to do their business before they scurried away; cats chased leaves and climbed lampposts. We didn't know the names of our neighbours, but we attached our own pet names. "Here comes Prissy Pants," I would whisper, pointing at a tidy lady who clicked in high-heeled mules to the curb every morning to retrieve her paper. Or, "Wonder if 'Beefer' will be able to bend over far enough to pick up *his* paper this morning?" we would giggle. Munching apples and peering between the rustling leaves, we soon felt the pulse of our neighbourhood.

Our side of the modest duplex, the south side, shared the same green roof as a dour couple who had lost their smiles many years ago. "Miserable as sin, they are," Dad whispered to us. He said he thought the old man, Mr. Gray, had inhaled too many fumes at the gas station downtown where he filled his shiny black Oldsmobile. The gas station had a big, lighted sign that said "–HELL," and as you came into town from the west hill, it was all the way at the bottom of the street, and it looked like that's exactly where you were headed. The sign had shed its "S" long ago and was the joke of the town, but no one cared enough to fix it.

The Grays soon made it known that they disliked children and were always complaining about us one way or another. They complained about the slamming screen door and our loud voices, and we learned never, never to touch the Olds. Mom told us to mind our p's and q's and not to disturb them. It became a ritual to stick out our tongues in their general direction every time we raced through the front door (our small protest). It was a good thing a green slatted wall separated the two verandas.

On the other side, not the duplex side, another older couple, the Dicksons, lived, but they always wore smiles and took time to stop and do little things like adjust the seat on my bike or fold my pant legs into my bicycle clip. Mr. Dickson would shift his pipe, push his glasses back on the bridge of his nose, and ponder every task with several *hmm's* and *ah's*. His pockets held endless mints (you had to remember to blow the lint off them first before putting them in your mouth). He raised himself up straight and snapped his braces every time he completed a chore. "Now, that's taken care of," he always said, then spat brown stuff on the ground. Mom said he chewed disgusting tobacco.

Across the street, a lighter-coloured brick house reached as high as the sky. Skirted with a majestic curved veranda supported by cream-coloured pillars, that house held a particular fascination for Ray and me. The perfectly trimmed hedge and carefully placed flowers along the walkway greeted no one coming or going.

Two doors farther down, on our side of the street, beyond the Dicksons', was a paint-deprived two-story frame that led us to pause and gawk every time we strolled past. This house was always busy with the goings-on of a family with three teen-age sons. The oldest one drove a motorcycle! He would sit revving it in the driveway before he roared away, always leaning at a crazy angle to the road. Ray and I dreamed aloud about getting a ride on that bike.

Bloomsgrove Avenue, with its mixture of neat, small houses tucked in among large, noble homes was typical of Port Hope. Ray and I continued to watch the street from the cover of the trumpet vine until the day Leo came to call.

Leo settled his squat, sturdy body at the bottom of the steps with legs apart, feet braced defiantly, his hands shoved firmly into the hip pockets of faded, tattered jeans. He rocked from one foot to the other, emphasizing his authority and claim to long-term residency.

"Hey, you the new kids?" he asked without waiting for an answer. "I live across the street," he indicated with a toss of his shaggy head. "M' mom says I have to ask you to play with me. So do you wanna?"

Ray eased out from behind the curtain of vine twirling a vivid red trumpet flower in his fingers. His long legs covered the distance to the top of the steps in four strides. He shrugged his shoulders as he pushed back a shock of straight blond hair that refused to stay off his forehead and constantly flopped over his eyes. With the aloof air of an eleven-year-old, he stared down at Leo.

"Maybe. What do you want to do?"

"Kick-the-can? Or if you play allies? We could play for keepers."

Ray stood for a minute, his hazel eyes deep in thought. Allies would be his preference, but he was a "ringer," and something told him that winning prize marbles from our new acquaintance would be a bad beginning. He looked Leo up and down and took in his kitchen-butchered haircut, ragged and chewed by scissors that were too dull, his jeans torn at the knees, frayed cuffs brushing the tops of loafers that had no memory of polish, and decided that Leo was a scrapper and clearly a year or two younger than him. "Kick-the-can sounds good. Can Molly play?"

Ray swung his arm, beckoning me forward from the protection of the vines. Holding my glossy black waist-length pigtails in one hand and brushing dusty white paint chips off my pinafore with the other, I cautiously peered at Leo. With a shy wave I said, "Hi, I'm Molly."

"Leo."

"Ray," offered my brother.

In a sudden burst, Leo tore off across the street, hollering that he would be right back with a can and other players.

I stepped toward #19, and the past drifted to me. The tall, bushy hydrangea tree that used to hug the walkway and scatter pink confetti petals all over the yard was gone, as was the trumpet vine. The veranda was boarded over with a sun porch. The other half was as I remembered. I saw myself and Ray joining Leo and others to play kick-the-can and heard the giddy squeals as if the street were filled with playful children as it was then.

And so our life in Port Hope began. It was a time when children were kids of the street, but in a good way. There were no parks engineered to perfection or grassy areas set aside for neighbourhood games. The roadway was our playground, and we accommodated the few cars that had to use it, or they understandingly let the play finish. In the beginning, our territory was limited to one block east to Hope Street, three south to Ward Street, one west to Ontario Street, and north to Ellen Street. All that was needed was a quick shout through the door to Mom giving our approximate location, and we were free to

OUR HOUSE.

venture anywhere within our boundaries. Everyone, except Leo, had a veranda, and our daily plans would be decided on a regular basis on one veranda or another. Patti came into my life and became my best friend. Ray, no longer angry that we had moved, hooked up with Dougy from up the street.

I soon had four friends on Bloomsgrove Avenue. Patti lived the farthest away, at #1 Bloomsgrove.

I decided to walk there. The houses had changed little in all those years. The Dicksons' house had cream trim now instead of white, and brown shingles instead of green. A modern garage, all neat and tidy, was a glaring contrast to the Dicksons', where scattered tools and belongings were always a discovery challenge. A curved, inlaid brick walkway now led to the front door.

Siding covered the chipped paint where the Harley motorcycle had lived. I gasped as I approached the willow tree that still lived three doors farther down. Memories of playing "house" beneath its branches were as vivid as if I were still there pouring pretend tea.

Donna banged on the open screen door then yelled through it. "Molly, come on. Patti got a new cutout book — Roy Rogers and Dale Evans! It's even got a saddle to put on Trigger!"

I raced out the door, grabbing an apple out of the basket on the counter, and followed Donna and Patti to our private hideaway beneath the old willow on Donna's lawn. The branches hung to the ground and created a shelter where light filtered through the soft green leaves. Under its protection, our imaginations took us on domestic and worldly adventures. When we parted the curtain of lacy branches, we entered our private, secret place. We shared picnics, played out movie star romances with our cutouts (Moira Shearer was my all-time favourite), sang, played clapping games, and gossiped little-girl gossip. It was a magical place. Donna's father, knowing its importance, let the branches fall to ground level, trimmed them neatly, and raked the "meeting place" clear of dried leaves.

"Let's build a corral for Trigger. Look, Roy has a lasso," offered Patti, proudly showing off her latest toy. "Can't you just see him catching a bandit or a train robber?"

"Hey, you gals playing with sissy paper dolls again?"

Leo and Billy, his buddy, leaned in through the leaf curtain.

"Get out of here! No boys allowed!" screamed Donna. Billy grabbed Trigger, and the saddle ripped away, tearing in two. Donna dove for the two intruders and hurled herself at Leo. To have invaded our willow shelter and abused our toys was a call to war. Patti and I joined Donna and jeered our disapproval of boys in general.

"Snot-nosed bucket heads!"

"Sissy prissies!"

Donna launched herself at Billy and drove him headfirst into the sidewalk. A scream that would terrify the banshees (my dad had explained all about banshees) ripped from his throat and we watched in horror as blood poured from his nose. Donna's mother, having been alerted by the commotion, rushed to the scene armed with a wet tea towel and shoved it under Billy's nose.

"Billy Trotter, you get on home and put some ice on the back of your neck and stay away from these girls. You come looking for trouble and trouble is what you get. Now git!" With that, she turned on her heel and disappeared into the house.

Back under the willow canopy, a bad case of the giggles had us clutching our stomachs and hashing and rehashing the victory of Donna's tackle. We patched up Trigger's saddle and played out all the moves and dialogue of Roy's latest movie, *Cowboy and the Señorita*. Donna's mother brought lemonade and cookies to celebrate.

Today the old willow was not trimmed but hung unkempt and lonely. I gathered a trailing branch and let the leaves slip across my palm then slide away. I wandered to the corner store that was wedged on a triangle between Bloomsgrove Avenue and Ontario Street. Now it is a convenience store, still serving the needs of the neighbourhood.

I was only allowed to go to the store with Ray or Mom. Mom would send Ray and me to cash in coupons to get butter or sugar. It was wartime, and certain goods were rationed. We always came away with a licorice pipe each, compliments of Mr. Miller, the owner. By the time we got home, the pipes were gone, but our lips and tongues were black for hours.

Eleanor, with her chubby cheeks and black bouncing curls, lived directly across the street from us at #22, and Becky (a slender wisp of a thing, my father always said) lived two doors down. Her father had gone to war. So had Leo's. We didn't see much of Leo, and when we did, he was a downright nuisance. He ran with a gang from up College Street way most of the time but always reappeared in the evening for kick-the-can or hide-and-seek.

Early evening activities occurred in front of our house, out on the roadway. The gentle evening air was regularly shattered with raucous calls of "Get it!" "Deke him out!" "Kick it — kick it!" of kick-the-can, or calls of, "Here I come, ready or not!" as we played hide-and-seek. Parents and neighbours gathered on our steps to chat and watch us while they sipped Hires root beer or chewed Doublemint gum until it was flavourless. Ray was tall and fast, so he became captain of one team, and Dougy, Ray's friend, was captain of the other. Ray's team was called the "Rangers," and Dougy's, the "Giants." It was a ritual to choose the teams. Each captain drew a broom straw for first pick. Best players were picked first. Leo was always first, me last. I learned later it was because I was the youngest and a girl.

I sure *tried* to get the can, but always some big foot scooped it just as I was lining up to give it a swift kick. My parents claimed that what I lacked in skills, I made up for in exuberance. It was their way of saying I was very loud. One night I ran after the can, ducked under Dougy's right elbow, and hit the can true with the toe of my runner. It slid right in for the winning goal. Everyone cheered. Can you imagine? Screaming with pride, I rushed to tell Mom.

"That's wonderful, Mollikins [oh, how I hated Mollikins!]," she said, hardly looking at me, and went back to the hushed conversation with the Baxters, Patti's parents. I just knew it was "war" talk — it always was.

It was 1944, and war was rampaging across Europe, but life in Ontario was distanced and untouched except for the whisperings of adults about places with strange names and the comings and goings of men and women in uniform. Patti's dad had just returned from someplace called Borneo. He didn't look too good to me. Someone said he had malaria, whatever that was.

Anyway, Ray chose me first for the next game! Life in our new town wasn't so bad after all!

❈ 2 ❈

JULY 1944

Walton Street looked almost the same as it had sixty-five years ago, except the railway tracks that had once cut across Walton and up Ontario streets were gone, and stores that, in 1944, served the townspeople were now boutiques beckoning inquisitive tourists. I gazed out the window of a trendy café and heard sounds from long ago, sounds of the Calithumpian[1] parade.

Ray enrolled in the Boy Scouts, Pack 33, the first week we arrived in Port Hope. He had been an active Boy Scout in Huntsville and that had been his major concern when leaving and moving to a new town: he was almost qualified to receive his "King's Scout" lanyard. He had lots and lots of badges sewn on the sleeves of his uniform. He had to iron his own stuff, too — his shirt and trousers, and especially his scarf. That's what you learn in Boy Scouts. His very first Scout duty in Port Hope was to march in the Calithumpian Parade.

"What's Calith — ... Calli — ... that word?" I asked.

"Hey squirt, it is Calithumpian, Cal-i-thum-pi-an," Ray offered with mock distain. "Little sisters are such a nuisance and so stupid. It's on Dominion Day."

"When's Dominion Day and what is that, anyway?" I set Janice on a chair and leaned in, eager to hear all about any parade.

"You know — Canada's birthday, July 1st. Only, there's no gifts, just a big party."

"Cake?"

"Think so. Wait and see."

Over the next few weeks, Dad came home with lots of talk about the parade. It sure sounded boring to me, because he talked about street closures and traffic management. But then the word on the street got really interesting. Patti, Donna, and Beth talked about

---

1   Calithumpian means BIG!

floats decorated like scenes from storybooks, bands playing loud music while they were marching, and horses with real cowboys and cowgirls. That was more like it! I shared this exciting news with my doll, Janice, and told her how much I wanted to go to the parade. Two days before Dominion Day, Dad arrived home calling my name as he slammed the screen door. Cautiously, I rose from the table where I was crayoning pictures in my movie star colouring book, grabbed Janice for security, and headed down the hall.

"Would you like to ride on one of the floats?" Dad said as he swung me and Janice high over his head. "The firefighters want to include some children on their float and need volunteers. Since your mother will be working the phones at the Police Station, and I will be busy with traffic," explained Dad, "I volunteered you. That way you can be looked after, see the parade, and be a part of it, too."

Would I, holy smokes, would I? With a "You bet!" I raced out into the street to find my friends and brag my big news.

"Calith —, Calithump —, Calithumpian, Calithumpian," I practised as I tore off to Donna's house.

Dominion Day arrived after the longest two days ever, and with the elastic bands on my braids wound tight and my face shining from Mom's wielding a rough face cloth, Dad drove me to the police station, which was attached to the fire hall. Dave, the fire chief, handed me a pink, frilly dress to put on over my shorts and top, placed a crown on my head, and called me the Firefighter's Princess. He swung me up into the oldest, shiniest, reddest fire engine at the station. A freckle-faced boy, chomping on a wad of bubble gum, was already there.

"Meet Bernie, my nephew," hollered Fireman Dave as he jumped up on the driver's seat. We drove all the way up the Walton Street hill to the end of Ridout, halfway across town. Ridout was lined with tractors, wagons, horses, funny little cars with clowns, and lots and lots of people wearing costumes. Bernie and I climbed up to the top of the water tank on the back of an antique fire truck and watched everything. There was so much to see with everything and everybody decked out. I saw cowboys with high-heeled boots and chaps tipping their ten-gallon hats to the ladies, little princesses and grown-up princesses with glittering crowns, and clusters of clowns standing around smoking cigarettes. There were lots of soldiers in uniform (navy, army, and air force), Scouts of all shapes and sizes,

Girl Guides, and grown-ups busy doing something or other. It was a mass of dressed-up characters rushing here and there, vehicles, animals, friends hailing each other, and just plain confusion, accompanied by bleating trombones and other instruments tooting for no apparent reason. I could smell sweaty horses, motor fuel, and sweet flowers from the assorted floats.

I was sure the parade would never get started, and all this muddle of people, machines, and animals would just keep churning faster and faster until they spun themselves into a colourful, molten blob. Finally, the big new fire engine arrived, with its bell clanging and horn blaring. It drove up to the front of the straggling line of tractors and trucks, bands and horses. People scattered here and there to let it pass. It let out two loud blasts. Incredibly, everyone scrambled to their places; Scouts suddenly were in a neat formation, bands stood ready to go, and all the dressed-up characters disappeared, to reappear on their proper floats. A large man wearing a red coat and a black top hat raced alongside the floats to the back of the line, blowing a whistle and waving a pad of paper. Then he stopped, raised his arm, and waved at the head fire engine. The parade was ready to go!

The new fire engine wailed its sirens, announcing across town that we were making our way down the hill to the centre of town. The old fire engine I was on only had bells, but Bernie and I got to keep them clanging like crazy. We could see people along the street. Eager spectators crowded the sidewalks all along the curbs of Walton Street. Freshly scrubbed little kids were sitting on the edge or riding on their father's shoulders. Balloon-holding families stood grouped with the taller members behind and the shorter ones in front, so everyone could see. There were even some people in wheelchairs and babies in carriages.

The sirens stopped suddenly, and immediately the bands struck up and marched smartly in unison. A whole flock of majorettes wearing glittering hats stepped high, their shiny red skirts swinging one way then the other. They tossed sparkling batons high in the sky and with knees bent high caught them every time mid-stride! Tractors sporting every colour of crepe paper streamers and decked in swags of flowers jerked along between the bands. Some had stuffed animals and some had real live dogs or cats; one even had a goat, and most had the Union Jack[2] flying high. There were cars and small trucks with signs advertising local businesses, and others just had people on them waving like crazy.

The clowns rode around in silly little cars that couldn't seem to go in a straight line. They threw saltwater taffy candies to the children. I waved and waved . . . after all, wasn't I the Firefighter Princess waving to my kingdom? Bernie let out shrieking whistles and waved, too. He was dressed as a cowboy. Trucks blew their horns at gyrating arms and crept along carefully so they didn't hit any of the children scrambling for candies that fell to the roadside. Friendly faces waved flags out of windows at us from the apartments above stores, and everyone clapped and cheered. Soldiers, sailors, and airmen marched smartly and they all turned their heads at the same time when they heard their commander give a loud "Eyes right!" as they passed the mayor standing on a tall wooden platform. I saw old people and lots and lots of children with their families, all with big smiles; everyone was waving flags or just waving. I even saw young men and boys hanging off telephone poles, just so they could get a better look at us. Donna and Patti screamed my name, and I waved as hard as I could at them until my crown tipped over my eyes.

Turning onto Queen Street, we continued past the town hall and pulled up in the back parking lot. Everyone swarmed off their floats and out of their trucks. The parade was over. Fireman Dave swung me down still flushed with the excitement of it all, with a "There you go, Princess." Mom and Ray arrived just as I was beginning to feel a little lost and alone, surrounded by strangers. We set out for the bandshell to hear the mayor speak. Kewpie dolls, monkeys on sticks, cotton candy, and oh, so many other tempting things were displayed in little booths lining the park all the way to the bandshell. Mom had to drag me along, as I wanted to gawk at all the good stuff on display. She explained how important it was to set a good example, being the chief of police's family, and that we had to stand quietly while the mayor and several other dignitaries spoke. He spoke, we behaved, a preacher prayed, and then we sang "God Save the King."

Mom sent Ray and me off and instructed us where to meet. She gave me twenty-five cents to spend! I had passed a cotton candy booth and I knew that I had to buy pink cotton candy, my absolute

---

2   The national flag of the United Kingdom.

favourite treat. Eager to bite into the sweet, pink froth, I raced to the booth. Jumping up and down in order to see over the counter, I watched the machine spinning the taffy. The cotton-candy man picked up a long paper tube and stuck it into the machine. Pink floss wound its way onto the tube, growing into a mass of fluff. Handing it to me, the man said, "Ten cents, please." I stared at the fifteen cents' change before shoving it into my pocket. A chunk of the spun candy sat on my tongue melting, sweet and delicious.

But I still had fifteen cents left! Fifteen cents to spend however I wanted! Donna and Patti appeared, and we wandered back and forth most of the afternoon, visiting all those booths and trying to decide on the best way to spend our money. Finally, I chose a miniature china baby dressed in a silk nightie and a little lacey cloth cap. She lay on a satin pillow and her arms moved. She was so tiny she fit in the palm of my hand. Donna and Patti bought Kewpie dolls. Mother arrived at the meeting place, took one look at me then spit into the ever-ready handkerchief to wipe the stuck-on bits of cotton candy glued to my cheek.

"Nothing like spit and the corner of a hanky to get a little girl looking spit-spot. Now, Mollikins [would she never learn how I hate Mollikins], Ray, I'm taking you home for a rest. We want you to be wide awake for the fireworks tonight, don't we?"

All the way home, I chattered on about the clowns, the peanut man from Planters, the big, big tire on the gas station truck, the other princesses, and how next year I wanted to be a princess again. Mother finally placed her hand over my mouth with a "Hush, too much blather, child!" Even though I knew I would never, never sleep — I was just not tired — I was put in my room anyway.

When Mom shook me awake, my bedroom light was on, and it was dark as anything outside. The edges of her eyes were kind of squished together like they were when she thought something was funny. "My little girl was sure played out. Pretty tiring being a celebrity, huh? Get dressed now, and put on a sweater, as it will be cool at the beach."

"We're going to the beach? It's dark out!" I exclaimed.

"I know. All the better for fireworks," laughed Mom.

I watched as she left my room. The smell of fresh-air laundry lingered behind. I seldom saw Mom in slacks, but this evening she wore dark green ones with a lighter green angora sweater. I knew it was angora because Mom told me so, and she always put it in the icebox to fluff it up before wearing it. Vagrant blonde curls escaped her floral kerchief rolled up like a colourful ribbon and tied in a bow at the top of her head. This was how she dressed when we went on a picnic!

I scrambled to my feet, threw on a pink woolly sweater and old navy corduroy pants, grabbed my socks and runners, and headed downstairs. I nearly collided with Ray as he ripped out of the bathroom. "Hey, squirt, watch where you're going."

"Yeah. Like it's me who's blind," I jibed back.

When we got to the beach, the whole town was there. People were laughing and chatting happy talk. I could smell stale beer mixed with the smell of rotting smelt and seaweed. I didn't care, because here I was, up in the middle of the night! Waves were sliding toward the shore, catching the silver of moonlight as they rushed forward to the sand then eased away to the other side of the lake, to Rochester. Dad gave a wave and indicated a prime spot he had staked out. There were certainly some benefits to being the family of the police chief!

Dave, the fire chief, got up in front of the crowd and said some words about how we were proud to be Canadian and that he and his crew had, for the safety of all of us, aimed the fireworks over Lake Ontario. The next thing I knew, I heard a whistle and then a bang. The whole lake lit up bright green, then white, then red. One after another, rockets, starbursts, and explosions just kept coming. Mom clapped and clapped, "always a sucker for fireworks," she explained. The smell of striking matches was everywhere, "from the fireworks, cordite," Mom explained to my question. Someone started singing the "Maple Leaf Forever" and everyone joined in. Songs and laughter filled the air between the noise of the fireworks. Then, I don't know how they did it, but a whole bunch of explosions popped all around us and "Happy Birthday Canada" appeared in bright red, white, and blue, out over the water. Everyone clapped and cheered. Then all went quiet. Hushed tones resumed as townspeople wandered toward their cars.

We slogged through the sand and emptied our shoes before getting into our old "Lizzie" to drive uptown to the fire hall for hotdogs and Freshie. And cake! Yep, the biggest cake I ever saw, and it was decorated just like the Union Jack. It was really late at night, but there were more people on the streets than I ever saw in the daytime. The street lights weren't on, because of the blackout imposed by the war, but flashlights weaved along, showing the way. I claimed Dominion Day as my all-time favourite day of the year, except for maybe my birthday or Christmas. Anyway, it was certainly the very best day of my first month in Port Hope.

❊ **3** ❊

STILL JULY 1944

*S*tepping away from the café, I wandered into an antique shop. My
heart skipped a beat. Hanging behind the counter was one of my
dad's paintings. Dad always dabbled in oil painting and when he
retired from the police force, he painted seriously. His work is well
known locally. With the painting, one of his deep-in-the-woods scenes,
wrapped in brown paper and held tightly, I returned to my car and
drove to Choate's Woods.

"Your house always smells funny!" exclaimed Donna, wrinkling up
her freckled nose.

"Yeah, I know — turpentine, linseed oil, and developer. My dad
paints and does photography," I replied.

"What's he paint?" she inquired while running her fingers
through a mop of dark, wayward curls.

"C'mon, I'll show you. Follow me. He has his doghouse in the
basement."

"Doghouse!"

"Well, Mom always calls it that. I think it is a grown-up joke.
Famous artists have studios, but my dad just works where he can.
Anyway it is a space he has set up beside the furnace, right at the back
of the house under the back window. He also shares the laundry tubs
with Mom so he can develop negatives and print photographs. He
has an enlarger and everything.

"It's called a darkroom because the lights have to be turned off
so as not to harm the developing pictures, and there is a special little
red light hanging over the sink to see by. Red lights don't bother the
pictures. Ray and I get to watch lots of times. It's weird how the red
light makes everything look, and a real mystery how a blank piece of
paper goes into the developer solution and after a few minutes a picture appears. Then Dad puts it in a fixative bath and hangs it to dry."

Patti was not paying any attention to any of my words of wisdom; she just had her nose wrinkled up at the smells.

"The light switch is at the bottom. Mom always says that someone is going to kill themselves trying to get to the light switch. Wait a minute while I stand on the bottom step and reach the chain." Standing on tippy toes, I stretched my arms out from my body until my fingers clamped around a cord hanging from the ceiling, then pulled.

Once I had turned on the dim, bare light bulb, a grim concrete world dared us to venture farther. Shadows, dark and menacing, threw changing shapes to damp corners that harboured spiders and other crawly things; orange and brown water stains ran down the walls near water pipes snaking up the walls and across the ceiling. A monster coal furnace loomed to the left of us, threatening us with its fierce, dark, hulking shape. For some reason, I feared that huge presence with its blackened sides and never-ending pipes stretching like muscled arms reaching into the dark shadows. I was afraid they would twist around and grab me.

"Yuck! That awful smell's worse down here. What is it?" demanded Donna as she inched down the steps, putting one skinny leg before the other and being careful not to let her red, yellow, and green plaid skirt brush against the walls. Her dark green sweater already had a smear of white from the concrete.

"Everything. Turpentine, Javel water, laundry soap, coal dust, and damp concrete — all those things," I replied with authority. "Mom is always opening the window and putting the fan on to clear the air."

The forbidden hole, the coal bin, was just ahead. It was like a small room with a layer of black dust and a few chunks of coal lying on the bottom. A small metal window, the chute, opened to the driveway. Mom told me the coal truck backed in and hooked up a long slide kind of thing to drop the coal from the truck into the basement bin. There were take-away boards at the opening to the basement side of the bin that were removed one board at a time as the coal disappeared into the hungry mouth of the furnace monster. Right now, the boards were up as high as they would go. The bin was closed off for the summer, and we were warned that it was off limits, as it was "filthy."

Taking Donna's hand, I moved her quickly around the back of the dreaded furnace. There, the cellar opened up and light shone in through two windows, one facing the backyard and one the driveway.

"Mom does her laundry over here and over there," I pointed. "See that easel? That's where Dad paints." I led her toward the window to see the work that was in progress. Donna barely glanced at the painting of a winter stream, turquoise in the morning light as it wandered through snowbanks, her blue eyes darting about, searching for a way out of the gloomy basement.

A new smell of fresh-baked cookies enticed us back upstairs and to the kitchen table. Still hot from the oven, we blew on our oatmeal cookies and washed them down with glasses of cold water. Crayons and colouring books were set out, and we bent to create masterpieces of our own.

Saturday, I wakened to a bright morning full of sunshine and when I scampered into the kitchen for my bowl of Cream of Wheat sweetened with brown sugar, Mom was at the counter packing food into the picnic hamper.

"Wher' 'e goin'?" I asked with my mouth full of cereal.

"Dad wants to do some sketching at Choates Woods. I thought it would be a great excuse for a picnic. Then we might go off to Garden Hill for a bit to see the Tuppers."

"Mmph, good."

The Tuppers had a small house in the country, and Dad had met them the first weekend we were in Northumberland County; that's where Port Hope is — in Northumberland County. They raised pigmy goats, and Mrs. Tupper made wicked brownies, so it wasn't hard to convince me that this was going to be a special day. I wolfed down my breakfast and headed for the hallway.

"Hold it, young lady," I heard. "Drink your milk."

Milk was always an issue. I disliked the taste and even when it was doctored with chocolate or strawberry flavouring, it still had that lingering, slimy taste. Holding my nose, I forced the white liquid down then darted for the door.

I had received a Brownie box camera for my birthday the previous March and I definitely wanted to get some pictures of the goats and animals at the Tuppers. I reached for the camera and my last roll of Kodak 127 film. I closed my bedroom curtains and took my camera into the clothes closet, the darkest place in the room. I opened the package and took out the film wrapped tightly in foil. Once I was sure it was dark enough, I unwrapped the film. I had been carefully instructed to avoid light of any kind while the camera back was open and the film was being rolled onto the spool. Holding the spool carefully so it did not escape and unravel, I slipped the tapered edge of the celluloid into the slot in the camera spool, making sure the cogs caught, rolled it forward, settled the new roll into its place, rolled the film tight, and closed the back of the camera. Peering through the small, red peephole in the back of the camera, I rolled the film to "1." It was ready for action.

I backed out of the closet, walked across the room, and drew back the pink flowered curtains before throwing on some old jeans and a cotton shirt. Instructions from the kitchen told me to make my bed and tidy my room. Picking my pajamas up off the floor, I rolled them into a ball and shoved them beneath my pillow. I pulled the pink chenille bedspread, with its scattered flowers worn to threads in spots, up over the tangled sheets and glanced up at my guardian owl. When we first moved to Bloomsgrove Avenue, I suffered terror dreams, probably caused by the trumpet vines tapping at the window. Dad cut the vines back, and Mom painted a picture of an owl that she hung over the head of my bed — my guardian owl that was to always watch over me. My terror dreams stopped.

Honking noises from the driveway hurled me into action. I grabbed my camera and bolted down the stairs and out the door. I wasn't worried about getting sick, as our destination was only minutes away, just on the edge of town.

Choates Woods was a grove of sugar maples. As we pulled up to the fence, the smells of earth warming from the previous night's shower filled the air. We weren't very deep into the woods before Dad set up his tripod and camera.

"What are you shooting?" I asked, because to me it was simply a lane with lots of trees.

"Look at the colour . . . the wet leaves. The morning light just glows, each leaf comes alive with varied tones of green and yellow. I need to capture that on film so that when I add oil paints to my sketch, I will have a record of the light and colour we are seeing now. Light changes everything." Through his eyes, I saw.

Mother, Ray, and I wandered on. Mom knew a whole bunch about wild flowers, lichens, mushrooms, and everything. She knew just where to find them, so our ventures into any woods were always discovery trips. We found jack-in-the-pulpits and dog-toothed violets, examined some moss, and gathered hickory nuts.

"Oh, my! Children!" We heard Mom draw in a long breath. "Be careful. What a treat! Look! Lady's slippers."

She was pointing at a cluster of funny-shaped pink flowers hanging like lanterns. The leafy green stems were poking through composting leaves. She knelt down and cupped a blossom in her hand and explained that the flower was a rare wild orchid, known as a Lady's slipper because it really looked like a sort of shoe. She then took pictures with her camera. As you may have already figured out, we were a picture-taking family: Dad, scenery; Mom, flowers; Ray and I, friends and animals.

We spent many Saturdays this way, and through Mom's enthusiasm and knowledge about everything in nature, Ray and I learned to identify many trees and flowers. We came to know different birds and how to tell the males from the females. We were taught the cycles of nature and to respect the privilege of sharing it. In just the short time we had lived in Port Hope, we had gone to Rice Lake, Northumberland Forest, Lake Ontario, and every interesting copse of trees that caught my parents' fancy.

The sun was high, and we selected a grassy spot for our picnic of cucumber sandwiches and peanut butter cookies. Mom had made fresh lemonade and sliced watermelon to round out the meal. When we were finished, we carefully folded the wax paper to reuse, packed up, and headed to Garden Hill.

There is a stream with a bridge and a maple woods right across the road from the Tupper place, and one day when Dad had been sitting at his easel painting a sketch of the stream, Mr. Tupper wandered over. "Curiosity got the best of me," he said. It seemed both he and my Dad loved to talk, so the talking began. And that is how they became friends.

The Tuppers greeted us with arms waving and broad smiles as we drove in through their grassy lane, then shook hands all around as we stepped out of the car. Mrs. Tupper was wearing a starched, flowered housedress partially hidden by the ever-present apron that reached down to her ankles. Today she wore a blue-flowered dress with a navy apron. Heavy, hand-knitted woollen socks rumpled down veined legs to scuffed brown oxfords. She wiped sudsy hands on her apron and grabbed my pigtails, giving them a friendly tug and commented on how brown I was getting. She smelled like fresh-baked bread.

Mr. Tupper tucked his hands inside the bib of his denim over-alls and grinned at both of us from behind a shaggy mustache. "New crop of kittens in the barn, and the ducks have new ones, too, over at the pond—"

The words were hardly out of his mouth before Ray and I lit across the backyard to the barn. The barn smelled of freshly scattered straw and heady goat manure. We knew the old tabby would have tucked her kittens in some secret place, so the hunt began. Ray signalled me to be still and quiet. We could hear a small mewing. It was joined by another, then another. We found them, a warm wriggling mass of fur, snuggled in the straw behind a feeding trough. When we separated them, they took on distinct features. Their eyes were barely open and they had bellies as big as the whole of them. Mommy cat pushed her way between us and tried to take charge. Laughing at her persistence, Ray and I cuddled her babies anyway before we relinquished them to her care. She stretched out, and each little mass of fur mewed its way to a nipple buried deep in her grey tabby fur. Then all was quiet except for mommy cat's purring lullaby.

Ray and I wandered out into the barnyard to see the little goats and laughed at their silly antics as they jumped and twisted and bounced on skinny legs, landing daintily on tiny hoofed feet. There were five all together: two brown, two white, and one with brown and white patches. Mommy goat ignored them completely, and the daddy was nowhere to be seen. The two brown ones suddenly took a stance to have a head-butting contest something like a tug-of-war backwards, pushing instead of pulling. Just as quickly, they started jumping about again, then flopped to the ground and settled into nap mode. Ray and I giggled as I snapped picture after picture.

We could see the pond in the distance and tore across the field to see the ducklings. "Muskovies," Mr. Tupper had told us on one visit, "and watch out—they can be mean." We watched from shore as the duck family circled the pond, led by Mommy with all the ducklings strung out behind. The drake was asleep on shore. Ray and I counted twelve little fluffy bodies and were thrilled as they drifted our way and started to come up on the lawn. Right then we knew the daddy was not asleep because he came charging at us with his white feathers all ruffled and his head stretched out in battle mode, aiming right for Ray and me, the red around his beak flaring hot. We took off in a flash back to the farmhouse.

"Just in time," announced Mrs. Tupper, setting out a heaping plate full of her mouth-watering brownies on the picnic table. "You just wash up at the pump, now, and hurry on back for a snack."

The breeze from two maple trees softened the summer heat, and with our tummies full of brownies and lemonade, Ray and I lay on the grass watching the bees humming around the honeysuckle and listening to the adults drone in the background.

"Mollikins!" called Mom. "Ray! Come here." We brushed loose grass off our pant legs as we dragged ourselves up off the grass and made our way to the picnic table. "Mr. and Mrs. Tupper asked if you would like to have a kitten —" No more was said as we danced around the table, screaming, "Yes, yes!"

Both Ray and I examined the batch of kittens, separated them and pointed at this one, then that one, trying to decide which kitten was the best. We deliberated for all of about fifteen minutes when one round-bellied ball of orange fluff staggered over to us and plopped at our knees. So it was decided. We were to return in two weeks, when the kittens were old enough to leave their mother, and bring "Marmalade" home. What a delicious thing to look forward to! We talked about nothing else all the way home.

4

AUGUST 1944 — SUMMER CAMP

returned to Walton Street and as I was parking the old Buick, a gentleman in a Scout uniform guided me into a vacant spot.

As I mentioned before, Ray was an avid Boy Scout. He did lots and lots of tests and if he did them well enough to make his scoutmaster happy, he got a little cloth badge that had a picture or symbol on it. Ray had badges all the way down his sleeve. They were all different — one had hands clasped, one had a little bonfire, another had a knotted rope — each one was for a skill Ray had conquered. Now, he was being considered as a King Scout, and, I was told, that was very special. In order to complete the requirements, he had to go to summer camp. Mom and Dad agreed that he could go, and not only that, Mom volunteered to be the camp cook. Since there was no place for me to be sent, I got to go, too.

The Scouts, their leaders, Mom and I, and another lady (she was the camp nurse) and her daughter got on a school bus at the town hall to go to the camp. We drove out of town, over the highway, and onto a bumpy road deep in the woods. We were headed up the Ganaraska, Mom told me. I was really proud of myself. I didn't get sick, but then again, we didn't go very far. Ray was probably also glad, because he would never have lived it down.

The country road, more like a country lane, was a dirt track with a crop of grass in the middle that brushed against the underside of the bus. It wound its way through Northumberland Forest before it broke out of the woods into a big meadow. There were two big tents beside a river, a big sand-coloured tent with open sides, and a small one right next to it.

The scoutmasters set the boys to pitching two rows of smaller sleeping tents and one tent set away to the other side. The big one was called the mess tent. I never really saw a mess in there except maybe on craft days, so maybe that is why it was called the mess tent.

Anyway, it was where we ate. The Boy Scouts slept six to a tent, and each tent had a leader. Each leader made sure everyone behaved and made up their bedrolls. They wore whistles around their necks and blew them to get the attention of those noisy Scouts.

Everyone called Mom "White Cloud" for some strange reason. Mom and I shared the all-by-itself tent with the camp nurse, who was being called "Tawny Owl." Her daughter's name was Helen. Mom called Tawny Owl "Ann" when we were away from the Scouts, and "Tawny Owl" when the Scouts were nearby.

We didn't have to sleep on the ground like the Scouts; we had cots to sleep on! We had to make up our beds and roll the blankets up into as small a bundle as we could. This was called a bedroll. We had to do it every morning, even though we weren't trying to get a badge or anything. Helen and I would help each other by laying the blankets and sheets out on the ground and rolling them up as a team. Then we set the bedroll across the bottom of the canvas bed and Tawny Owl inspected them just as if we were getting badges.

There were no bathrooms! The Scouts dug holes in the ground called latrines and they built a box over the hole. Some of the Scouts banged poles into the ground, and a sheet was tied to the poles so we couldn't see behind. Our tent had its own outhouse. Ray said he earned a carpentry badge because he helped build the latrines. One thing you learned really quickly was to check for spiderwebs across the hole! I sat on one and flew off that seat slapping my backside and dancing the spider away.

The first day at camp, we played games to learn about where we were, the camp rules, and each other's names. All the other grown-ups had weird names like "Great Wolf," "Mighty Beaver," and "Big Otter." The first night we were there, a wicked storm blew up and howled and crashed all around us. Tawny Owl was terrified of lightning, and Mom had to hold her just like she held me when I had a nightmare. We heard a great crashing sound right after lightning made the inside of our tent as bright as day. Tawny Owl screamed and started crying. Mom was kept busy calming her down, but Helen didn't wake up, and I was fascinated by a grown woman shaking and screaming with fright from something as natural as a storm.

Mighty Beaver ducked his head in through the flap. "The stove in the food tent has been hit by lightning! The chimney acted like a conductor rod and the force blew the stove to bits. The cook tent caught fire, but we put it out. Nothing else was destroyed, and nobody was hurt.

"We will assess the damage in the morning to see if we have to break camp. The storm seems to be over now, just a little rain. You might as well snuggle down for the remainder of the night. Good night." His head disappeared into the darkness.

Of course I had to pee, so Mom and I slogged through the mud with a flashlight, checked for spiders, and set to giggling over what might be down in the hole. In the morning, after lengthy discussions, it was decided that the stove could be fixed and another tent rigged; so instead of sending everyone home, we were able to stay. The weather behaved after that night.

The Ganaraska River was wide and deep at the camp, creating a good-sized swimming hole. Every afternoon, the Scouts had swimming lessons, and Helen and I were included while our mothers attended to other chores. I could already dog paddle a little distance, but I learned to do the back float. Big Otter taught me. He made me lie back with his hand on the back of my head. "Don't worry, if you slip under I will drag you back up by your pigtails." I knew he was kidding. He never did let me sink, and I soon learned to hold my tummy to the sky and relax. It was fun lying back and watching the trees waving at me as I floated around.

Ray was already a good swimmer and really liked to show off. One day, near the end of our last week there, he raced through the water, swimming to the far shore, and flopped on the green ground cover, laughing and challenging others.

"Ray, get out of there," Big Otter shouted. "Poison ivy!" Ray sure scurried out of there in a hurry. The next day, a red rash was spreading down Ray's back and across his tummy. One of the leaders — we never did learn which one — said the only way to cure a poison ivy rash was to rub boiled juice of the plant on it. This was done before my mother got wind of it or, as she said, she would have put a quick stop to *that*!

As if this weren't enough, the next morning, Ray came to breakfast with a large garter snake clasped in his hands. Apparently it had crawled into his sleeping bag during the night and wakened Ray as it was trying to crawl out in the morning.

"I felt something on my leg and when I unzipped the sleeping bag, his head lifted up and he hissed at me. I nearly wet my pants!" Well, that was the talk of the camp until later in the day when Tawny Owl nearly tripped over a skunk on her way to the "honey house" (that's what we called our outhouse). Luckily it didn't spray her, or our tent would have been off limits, not to mention the outhouse.

These adventures led to discussions on wildlife in the area and how to identify them. We all learned to look first before venturing down a path. By nighttime, Ray was very itchy, and no amount of Calamine lotion kept him from scratching.

Great Cloud wakened Mom in the middle of the night. Ray was very uncomfortable and had a very high temperature. Mom shook me awake and told me we were going home. Great Cloud drove us. By morning, Ray was very sick from the poison ivy and had to go to the doctor. Next thing we knew, Mom broke out in a rash from bathing Ray with cool cloths and wiping Calamine lotion on the rash. Matters got worse. Mom and Ray both had severe allergic reactions to the poison ivy and had to be admitted to the hospital. They were given a serum to combat the fever and poison. Ray improved overnight and came home, but Mom reacted to the serum and became very, very sick. It was really scary when Ray and I went to the hospital to see our ever-smiling mom just lying on the sheets, her smile gone, her fine, curly hair stringy and wet from sweat. Her skin was all red and swollen. We hardly knew it was her! I was sure she was going to die and I cried all the way home. We learned from that incident that Mom's system was sensitive to many drugs and we saw her endure violent reactions throughout her lifetime.

In spite of all this, Ray's rash cleared up, Mom did get better, and we all got to go to a special ceremony where Ray was awarded his lanyard signifying that he was a King Scout. I joined the Brownies.

The rest of the summer was spent going to the beach or playing on the street. Most times when we played on the street, we had a parade just like the Calithumpian, with costumes and all. We got all dressed up and paraded from Colliers', halfway up the street, all the way to Patti's at the bottom. We banged pot lids for cymbals, played toy drums, and I had a tambourine. All the neighbours came out to watch and cheered and clapped. We put on a good parade!

Port Hope Beach was way at the bottom of town, and Ray and I were not allowed to go there by ourselves. The parents on Bloomsgrove took turns taking us. Lake Ontario stretched out as far as one could see. The water rolled up in gentle waves on the sandy shore then slid back. Mom explained that water moved all the time and when it was rolling up over our toes, it was doing the same to a little girl on the other side of the lake, at Rochester, New York, in the United States. She also explained that the United States was another country and did not sing "God Save the King."

Patti and I raced along the hard-packed sand trying to outsmart the waves by jumping as they rolled in, to keep them from getting at our feet. The waves won every time. We just could not stay in the air long enough for them to roll out again. We loved to wade through the water's edge and kick spray as high as we could. We rolled in the sand then raced into the water to let the waves wash away the grit. We stomped on the wet sand to leave our foot imprints and watched the waves suck them away.

There was a lifeguard who sat way up high on a tall, skinny chair. Sometimes he would blow his whistle, and that meant everyone had to get out of the water. He watched all the time to make sure no one wandered into an area where Mom warned there was an undertow. We were warned and warned about that area and told not to go there. But there was always some stupid show-off who would tempt the water, and the lifeguard would have to get everyone out of the water, get down off his chair, and give that person a little talking to. We would have to wait until the lifeguard blew the "all clear" whistle before getting back in the water.

The pavilion, known as the "pav," a wooden building with faded green paint, stood at the back of the sand, near where everyone parked their cars and bikes. Right beside the pav was a play area with swings and a merry-go-round. Not the kind with horses and pigs, just a platform with metal bars that we grabbed and ran beside until it started to turn really fast, then we would jump on and ride it until it slowed down. It was our favourite thing to do.

One day, one of the big kids from across town told Patti and me to hop on and he got that merry-go-round spinning really fast. I got a little stupid and tried to jump off while it was turning. That's when I learned what a sand burn was. Mom doused me with pink Mercurochrome when I got home and told me not to try anything so silly again or the next time she would put iodine on the scrape. I was lucky — iodine really stung, not to mention it stank. The next time we went to the beach, a kid fell off the swings and broke his arm. He got to wear a neat plaster cast, but I only had pink smeared down my leg for a few days. Shaking her head, Mom said she didn't know how children got all grown up in one piece.

Mom walked along the sand with us on little adventure trips. Her sharp eyes always found a treasure or two: snail shells, clamshells, bits of smooth wood, and the most treasured of all, glass chunks that were etched white from the water. Mom told us that they were from ships that sank in the great lake almost a hundred years before. I collected bits and pieces — light green, dark green, dark blue, light blue, and amber. I saved them to play hopscotch. Hopscotch was something we did a lot. We would take a piece of chalk and draw the squares on the sidewalk then jump up and down on them until somebody won by collecting the most pieces of glass from the squares.

Days at the beach always ended with each of us licking a great big ice cream cone. We rushed to the pav to watch the ice cream man scoop deep into our favourite flavour and stack it three scoops high on the cone. Mine was always strawberry, or sometimes butterscotch, but only if it was the kind with lots of streaks of the sweet yellow goo. We usually sat on top of one of the picnic tables and licked away as we watched for big boats or were just mesmerized watching the light dance across the ripples before they slapped the shore and turned to foam. Cones finished, we had to rush back in the water to wash off the dripped ice cream that had run down our arms, bathing suits, and legs.

Sometimes we ventured farther out of town. Mom and Dad discovered a place called Keen. It was a native burial ground. Not many people knew about it, but Dad liked to sketch there, and we learned about how Indians buried their dead, and that the area was special, "sacred." We took that information and let our imaginations run away to cowboy and Indian days as we remembered them from Roy Rogers movies — especially if Patti or Donna came as our guests. We raced over the little hills and tumbled down the other side, to escape arrows flying through the air, and landed safely snuggled against the knoll. Our trusty steeds always came to our rescue in the nick of time.

Mom explained that the "hills" were not hills but burial mounds, and we needed to be more respectful of the people who were buried there. I wanted to know if there were any chiefs buried there and if they put their feathered headpieces in the ground with them like they did in Egyptian tombs. We had been to the Royal Ontario Museum and I saw all the treasures buried with the kings. "I don't think the tribes that lived here did that. It was important to them to pass down tradition, so the headdress went to the next chief," offered Ray. He had been studying about natives in school.

After a visit to Keen, we always stopped at Bewdley for a swim before heading home. Bewdley was on the highway between Rice Lake and a row of bait and tackle stores. There was a good ice cream stand. Sometimes Dad would rent a rowboat, and we got to go out for a boat ride. I had to wear a heavy life jacket that pinched my ears when it was pulled over my head. Sometimes we fished. I almost always caught lots of sunfish. Whenever one of us got a "bite," the rule was that everyone pulled in their lines until the catch was brought in. Sunfish were fun to catch because they wiggled sideways and leapt out of the water, their yellow and blue sides flashing brilliant in the sunlight. We put them back in the water most of the time. Dad took them off the hook very carefully so they weren't hurt. We watched them swim away, going deeper until they were no longer visible. Sometimes we took them home. "Good pan fish, sweet meat," Dad explained.

We had one other favourite place on Rice Lake — Gores Landing. There was a pier where we could leap off to swim or, on the other side, dangle our hook and line over to catch lake perch. But the main reason to go to Gores Landing was the restaurant. They served Mom's favourite foods, and, as Dad would say, "she deserves a day off." That didn't make sense to me, because Dad was the one who went to work — Mom was off all the time!

Water was certainly a large part of our summer days whether we were at Rice Lake, on the Ganaraska, or swimming in Lake Ontario. The summer days melted away.

5

STILL AUGUST 1944

I returned to #19, wandered up the front walk, and climbed the steps to the sun porch that used to be the veranda. No one answered my knock, but I took the liberty of entering the porch and peering through the front window. Visions of the living room as it had been those many years ago were as real as if it were still 1944.

Every Saturday evening, right after supper, Ray and I sat on the floor with our ear pressed against the brocade fabric stretched across the speakers at the bottom of the radio, waiting in anticipation for the creaking door and the announcement, "*The Shadow knows.*" With my chin firmly set on top of my clasped knees, I felt cold shivers run down my back and my neck tingle. My father, standing with one hand on the top of the radio, sent sweet wafts of pipe smoke our way. Mother leaned forward from the overstuffed chair, her darning stretched over a spent light bulb, idle on her lap. No one wanted to miss a word. After the bone-chilling broadcast, the family usually attacked a partially finished puzzle spread on the dining room table. The mystery epic was rehashed and rehashed. More than once someone would say, "only The Shadow knows . . ." in a creepy voice, then everyone would burst into laughter.

One time we gathered around the radio without Dad — just Ray, Mom, and I. We were very excited because my father was being interviewed by a radio journalist about some German prisoners he had captured. The Germans had escaped from an internment camp near Bowmanville. As a police chief, my father was deemed "essential service" and exempt from enlisting, but this did not mean that the conflict didn't reach him. Evening meals were lively with discussion: anything from schoolwork, Mother's activities, or Dad's work. Dad often told us about bulletins he had received about war issues, and this would lead to a discussion of current events.

He learned about the two escaped prisoners from one of these bulletins. Shortly after reading the bulletin, he was on Walton Street and spotted two men heading down an alley. Certain they were the escaped prisoners, he rounded them up. "They were no trouble," he said, "just hungry." Dad received a citation for capturing them, and the radio station thought it would make a good interview. There was some man on the radio talking all about it and how the prisoners had gone into the alley at the back of the Capitol Theatre, and, suspecting something out of the ordinary, he had stopped them to ask what they were doing there. I asked Mommy when Daddy would speak, and she looked surprised and explained that it *was* him speaking. It was the first time I realized my father had an Irish accent! Some explanation was needed, and I was told that I was so used to my father's voice that I didn't notice his Irish accent, but when it was broadcast, the radio waves changed the sound so that I noticed it.

When Dad got home, I was waiting to ask a lot of questions. He had a lot of explaining to do, as far as I was concerned. I wanted to know all about being Irish. That is when I learned about Ireland and what an Irish brogue was. He explained that he was from the north and didn't have a brogue but a lilt. Then he demonstrated the difference. It was much more interesting than talking about the war. He told me Ireland was known for its green, green grass, leprechauns, and the Blarney Stone. It sounded like a magical place.

I asked if he was a policeman in Ireland.

"Yes," he said. "I was a captain in the Royal Irish Constabulary."

"Did you catch any war criminals there?"

"Well, there is a different kind of conflict there. I did have a run-in with some nasty IRA men."

"What is IRA?"

"Irish Republican Army, a bunch of political rowdies who believe they should be running the country. That's why I left Ireland." His eyes were far away.

"What do you mean?"

"They were not nice fellows and they were very unhappy with me. They wanted to kill me. So I left. Came to Canada."

"Did they shoot you?" I gasped.

"Yes."

"Where?"

"Here," he said as he lifted his pant leg. An ugly red scar on his calf glared at me.

"But it didn't stop me from dancing," Dad said as he shoved the pant leg back down and jumped to his feet. "Every Irish lass should know how to do a little fling and the soft shoe."

The next thing I knew, we were touching toes to floor and jumping around the living room. I forgot all about war criminals and nasty IRA guys. Ireland and things Irish became the most interesting thing in my life for the next few weeks. I learned I had a grandmother there, cousins, and an aunt and an uncle. I knew I had some cousins and aunts in Toronto — Aunt Charlotte and Aunt Edna — my Dad's sisters, but there was another sister and a brother way over in Ireland! (Mom told me that Dad was close-mouthed about his life in Ireland, as if that explained everything.) I learned Irish songs; "Toora Loora Loora" was my favourite. I showed all my classmates where Ireland was on the map. My dad told me I was a true Irish colleen with my black hair, fair skin, and blue eyes.

I couldn't wait to visit my cousins in Toronto so I could tell them all about my newly discovered information. I wondered if they knew we had cousins in Ireland.

Sometimes I hid on the stairs and listened in on conversations between my mom and dad. That was how I heard we were going to Toronto. I stumbled down the rest of the stairs and burst through the kitchen door.

"When?" I screamed, jumping up and down.

"Settle down, young lady," commanded Mom. "Dad and I thought we would visit Grandma and your dad's family the last week of August. We might even get to the Canadian National Exhibition."

"What is the Canadian National Exhibition?" I asked.

"The CNE? It's a fair. It started as an agriculture fair, really, but it has changed. There are lots of rides *and* cotton candy!" She tweaked my cheek and gave me a hug. "Not that you like cotton candy. Your dad and I courted there."

"Courted? What's courted?"

Well, I learned many things that summer.

The trip to Toronto was pretty good — I only threw up in Bowman- ville. When we arrived, Grandma was busy bustling about and she set Mom to peeling pears and Ray and me to gathering them from the tree in the backyard. Dad and "Old Willy," my grandfather, disappeared into the sitting room, with Dad sucking on a pipe, and my grandfather a stinky old cigar.

Ray and I were full of questions about Grandma's budgies. She raised them in cages in the basement and always had a new hatch for us to peek at. We were not allowed to touch them, but Petie, a bright green budgie, lived upstairs and had the run of the place. Petie talked! Well, only a few words, but he could say "Hello" and "Kiss me," and called my grandmother "Lena." Petie would stride across the table when we were eating and steal bits of food or ride around on our shoulders and lean into our lips giving us lots and lots of kisses.

"Grandma, will you take your teeth out and put them in a glass tonight?"

"Molly!" my horrified mother scolded.

I discovered my grandmother's teeth in a glass beside the kitchen sink on our last visit, and Grandpa had chased me around the kitchen with them in his hand. "I'm going to bite you!" he teased. A stern Scotsman, we seldom saw this side of our grandfather. It was more than likely we heard things like, "Therrre'll be no talking at the table. When ye finish, sit with yourrr hands on yourrr lap until you arrre excused." His brogue was thick and his manner strict.

I forgot about the teeth when I heard my Uncle Bill calling from the hallway. "Hey, where are my favourite niece and nephew?" I ran screaming into his arms. After hugs and greetings all around, my uncle was instructed to take the kids somewhere. We knew that meant a walk to Eglington Avenue for ice cream. As we were heading up the street, my Aunt Nell approached from the streetcar stop. Sending Ray off with a package for Grandma and a "hurry and catch up," she joined us. I ate a whole chocolate fudge sundae all by myself!

"Billy and Nell!" chided mother when she heard about the sundaes. "You will spoil those kids rotten." She didn't sound real angry, though.

The late August evening grew chilly, and as the dishes were being cleared, Grandpa lit the fireplace. We all gathered, and Ray and I sat quietly as the grownups talked and talked. It was mostly talk of the war, and how everyone in the city was working for the war effort. Uncle Bill said his leave was up and he was due to ship out for another round of duty that very week. The room became very still and faces wooden. I saw a tear trickle from behind Grandma's glasses, but she caught it before it slid down her cheek.

Right then, Petie streaked across the room and flew right into the fireplace. Grandpa jumped and reached right into the flames, but was too late. "Lena, he should have been caged!" he yelled. "The little fool died instantly." It was a sad end to our almost perfect day, and I was angry with Grandpa for lighting the fire, but I just sulked and kept my angry thoughts to myself.

The next morning, sunshine poured through the lace curtains set in motion by the late summer breeze, and I lay in bed watching floral shadows dance across the walls. The kitchen was already bustling with activity when I ducked my bed-tossed head through the door. Smells of taters 'n onions made me rush to the table, starving for Grandma's soft-boiled eggs broken over the lightly fried potatoes and onions.

Two picnic baskets sat on the table and food wrapped in wax paper and tea towels lay strewn across the white tiled counter. It was Exhibition day! The crowded house was buzzing with "Wash your faces. Molly, bring me the hairbrush. Ray, clean your teeth." "Lena, I'm off to the train yard." "Jo, did you pack the apples?" "Kids, go wake your uncle, we want to get on our way." And finally we did. We got to ride on a streetcar, too. It clattered down Dundas Street, screeching to a stop at every corner as passengers got on and off. I got to pull the cable above my head when we got to the exhibition ground to tell the driver we wanted to get off.

The CNE grounds bordered Lake Ontario. It was magical, with the sounds of calliope, hawkers, and machinery, and smells of hot dogs and popcorn mixed with smells of hot people. It was a place where everyone could forget the war for a little while. Uncle Bill took Ray on the Ferris wheel, but I didn't trust my timid tummy to behave on that one! I rode and rode the merry-go-round, a real one with wild animals staring with unseeing eyes as they went round and round. I chose a tall white horse with a red saddle. We rode and rode to the strains of the calliope whining all around us. What a wonderful noise, what a wonderful steed!

We visited lots of buildings and saw farm animals, cakes, military stuff, and finally, just as I was starting to complain that I was

GRANDPARENTS

hungry, Aunt Nell bought pink cotton candy. At noon, we went to the lakeshore. Mom, Grandma, and Aunt Nell spread out the food on a red-checkered tablecloth on the grass and we ate and ate until we all said we were going to "bust." After lunch, there was an air show, and we watched airplanes streaking across the sky and doing great tricks. Uncle Bill knew every model, and he and Ray talked a lot about what each airplane was used for and how many types Uncle Bill had flown. One plane with two wings flew in close, and a woman climbed out on the wing and waved at the crowd!

After the air show, we returned to the midway and stayed until early evening. The colourful sights and music filled my head. Uncle Bill won a red teddy bear for me at the shooting gallery, and I got to have another ride on the merry-go-round, but this time I had to ride an elephant because some scummy kid already had my horse. I think I fell asleep on the streetcar, because I don't remember getting home to Grandma's.

The next day, we were off to see the Irish cousins. Most of them were already grown up, so I didn't really have a playmate cousin except Colleen. She was two years older than Ray, but she was always really nice to me and never treated me like a little kid. I asked her about being Irish and she just shrugged her shoulders and said both her parents were Irish, so it didn't mean anything to her. Well, there went my whole reason to see my cousins! We spent the rest of the afternoon saying "hello" and "goodbye" to several sets of families. Ray and I got to eat lots of cookies and I got to drink sweet tea. I had my head ruffled a lot before we went back to Grandma's.

"Grandma," I asked, "Dad was born in Ireland, so he is Irish, Mom was born in Canada, so she is Canadian. Grandpa is Scottish, so what are you?"

"Polish," she replied.

"What is Polish?" I asked.

"From Poland, but my passport says I am Austrian, because Poland was divided many times. My part was given over to Austria."

Right then, my mother's smiling face appeared through the back door. "And do you know what that makes you, Molly?"

"No, what?"

"A mongrel!"

❀ 6 ❀

SEPTEMBER 1944 —
SUMMER FADES INTO AUTUMN

I aimlessly wandered to the top of Bloomsgrove Avenue while thoughts about the final summer days when I was seven became moving pictures in my mind.

As the warm sunny days became shorter and the dark of night came earlier, talk shifted to the start of school. I wasn't too sure about going to a new school; scared to the other side of tomorrow is what I was. Dr. Powers School was three blocks back of us and we had only to cut through the fence two doors up, cross in front of the arena, head up Bob's Drive, cross the road, and in five minutes we would be there. Getting there was not what scared me — it was everything else. Sure, I had gone to Grade 1 in Huntsville, but Dr. Powers School in Port Hope was big and full of unknowns.

DR. POWERS SCHOOL

The first day of school, Mom, full of smiles, plaited my braids so tight it felt like she had managed to twist my scalp right into the weave. "I can't believe my baby is in Grade 2, almost grown up," she babbled. Dressed in a new navy blue jumper with big box pleats in the front, a starched white blouse, and new penny loafers without the penny, I slumped on the stool. Mom fussed over Ray, told him not to put his hands in his pockets, brushed his unruly forelock back, and continued to say wonderful things about our new school. Ray and I exchanged glances; this kind of run-on blather had us both as wary as could be!

Finally, Mom walked both Ray and me to the school, not through the fence, but up Bloomsgrove to Hope and along to the big red brick building with "Dr. Powers" written on it. We walked around to the front of the school. Dr. Powers School was a two-storey square red brick building with an annex off to the west side. An alleyway ran between the annex and the main building. The main entrance had concrete steps that led up to the front door. Mom barrelled up the steps, and Ray and I dragged behind. Ray muttered, "Thirteen steps, just like going to the gallows." I didn't quite get it, but Mom shot him a "Don't get smart!" look. Mom held open the large wooden double doors, searched for the office, found it off to the left, then motioned us to two chairs. We sat, with explicit instructions to be quiet and still, not to fidget, and especially not to kick at the chairs and scuff our new shoes.

I pushed at the pleats of my jumper, tugged at the cuffs of my socks, and ran my fingers around my collar to ease the scraping of the starch on my neck. My bottom was pins-and-needles numb before I looked up and saw a terrifying sight. She was a towering warlord. A drab brown skirt swung briskly from side to side, and the leather elbows of her tweed jacket were bent in determination as she bore down on us. I just knew she was coming for me! Sure enough, Miss Weldon was the Grade 2 teacher, and I was abandoned to her care. Ray, I learned later, went up *thirteen* more steps to some distant room.

The Grade 2 classroom was all the way at the far end of a dull green hallway that disappeared into darkness. Reluctantly, I tagged along beside Miss Weldon into that dismal corridor, the walls pressing inward. I turned to see my mother waving in the distance. Miss Weldon chattered constantly, but I heard no words. Finally, we reached a green door with "Grade 2, Miss Weldon" on a little card stuck in a brass holder. My tummy was doing nasty things, and my wobbly legs threatened to collapse. We entered a classroom of brown desks supporting the clasped hands of quiet boys and girls. Twenty heads turned and twenty pairs of eyes stared at me. I heard a distant voice say, "Class, this is Molly. She has just moved to Port Hope; let's make her welcome." A loud "Welcome, Molly" buzzed in my ears, and I felt myself being led to a desk. My stomach cramped and I was terrified I would puke all over my new pleated jumper and penny loafers. Tears burned and my nose started to run. I didn't have a tissue, so I just sucked in a great big sniff, ran my starched sleeve across my nose, and sank deep into the seat.

"Now, class, everyone stand and sing the national anthem and recite the pledge of allegiance." I choked. I did not know the pledge, but I did know some of the words of "God Save the King," although I couldn't squeak them out.

"I'm Lucy." A voice beside me penetrated my buzzing head, and I looked through misty eyes to see a smiling face, a lavender dress, and blonde curls. "Don't worry, you will soon learn them."

Lucy became my friend, and school became my favourite place. Miss Weldon turned out to be the best teacher ever, with a warm smile and always ready to help. She would spend time explaining little things and was never agitated by my frequent questions. I had a quick memory and a driving desire to be first, to get the highest marks in the class. My nearest competitor was Wallace Snowden, and he and I were head to head most of the time, with the top marks in the class. Wally would beat me in geography, but I had him in recitation.

That was the year I learned about the Kiwanis Festival. It took place in Peterborough, and students got to play the piano, sing, or do public speaking. Grade 2 did speeches or poetry, and we got to choose our own poems. Mom read stories and poems to us at home, and my favourite poem was "The Highwayman." Within weeks, I could recite "The Highwayman" from beginning to end. Mom explained what a casement was, and I flaunted my superior intelligence by explaining to the class how the innkeeper's daughter opened both panes and leaned out that particular kind of window to watch for her boyfriend, the Highwayman, which is really an old-time word that meant a thief who went charging down the road on his horse. Miss Weldon told me she thought my choice of poem was a strange selection for a policeman's daughter. I didn't understand why — my dad didn't ride a horse.

The war was discussed in school every day. We wrote letters and coloured pictures to send to the soldiers overseas. Apparently, letters and pictures made soldiers very happy. I drew a picture of a parade with me riding a float all dressed up like a princess. I even wrote "ME" on it with an arrow pointing to the princess. A big map on the side wall showed us where Europe was and where the war was in relation to Canada; Europe was brown and Canada pink. Miss Weldon would take her pointer and point to Port Hope, right on Lake Ontario, and drag her pointer all the way across pink Canada and the blue Atlantic Ocean to Europe. She tapped the pointer at England and Germany as if that would tell us exactly where they were. We just knew that the war was in a brown place, and our armed forces were right there, in that brown area fighting for something called democracy, and that they liked to get letters with pictures.

Some of the older classes learned to knit scarves to send to "the boys at the front." Most of the kids in my class had a father or an uncle in one of the services fighting somewhere over in that brown place. Emily lived with her grandmother because both her parents were there. Her dad was a doctor and her mother a nurse. My father couldn't go because he was something called "essential services." My mom's two brothers were in the air force. Yes, we knew what it was like to be at war: it meant writing letters and drawing pictures, listening to BBC, and looking at a brown place on a map where someone's dad, uncle, neighbour, or brother was fighting bad guys.

At home, we huddled around the radio in the living room to hear news of the "front." The static of the BBC buzzed a constant background noise in the house. Mom had monthly gatherings around the kitchen table, where the same eight ladies packed cardboard boxes with extra ration coupons, food, and clothing to help local families who were struggling while their men were away at war. Ray and I were sworn to secrecy about the parcels and we learned that many families of kids we knew and went to school with needed food and clothing.

We knew all about rations and saving string and foil. Meat, sugar, and butter were hard to get, because they were needed to send to the troops; therefore, Oleomargarine! Instead of butter, we spread this awful white stuff on toast and smothered it with molasses to kill the suet-like flavour. Some smart person decided that it would be taste better if it was the colour of butter, but the factory couldn't do that for some reason. They could supply the colouring, but not mix it in — something to do with butter producers thinking it would be too much like butter then and people would get confused. Fat chance of that! Anyway, a pound of Oleomargarine came in a plastic bag with a little packet of colouring powder set in the centre top just under the plastic. The packet of colour was dark orange, and the trick was to break the packet while it was still in the plastic bag and squeeze and squeeze the packet, mixing in the powder without leaving any reddish streaks. That was my job. I would knead and knead the little packet, determined that yellow had to taste better.

September is apple season, and Southern Ontario was known for its apple orchards. One bright, sunny Sunday, nothing would do but that we get into our jeans and rubber boots, pile into the old Ford, and head off to an orchard near Brighton. A bushel basket with a brown potato sack stuffed in it was sitting on the seat between Ray and me. A basket full of Mackintosh apples and a sack of Northern Spies was the objective, Macs for eating and Spies for cooking.

Ray was busy making a parachute out of a hanky, four pieces of string, and a rock. I was huddled against the door, hugging Janice, hoping the coolness of the metal would help keep my stomach in place. We stopped at the "–hell" station for gas, the fumes wafting over me. Heading south, we soon turned east onto Highway #2 and headed out of town toward our destination. Lake Ontario glinted between tall elm trees to the right; the bouncing sunlight on the water stung my eyes. Fields of buckwheat and corn spread out golden and green on the north side of the road as we headed east. Dad explained that buckwheat was planted every few years to give the soil a rest, and beekeepers put their hives there because the buckwheat blossoms were sweet with sugar. "Dad's family lived on a farm in Ireland and he knows about such things," Mom said. The cows were lazy, just standing by the fence people-watching beneath a row of bobbing crows on the telephone wires. Mother told us the story of Johnny Appleseed, we played "I Spy," and sang, "She'll be Comin' Round the Mountain" until my dad hollered at us to "Stop! Enough!"

When we got to Grafton, Dad turned sharply up a side road to "catch the light on a grove of maples" he saw at the last minute. When he swerved around the corner, I was leaning my elbows on the window frame, sucking in the fresh air. The door that I was propped up against popped its latch and flew open. The next thing I knew, I was out of the car flying in a heap headed for the ditch. The ground hit me hard, and I rolled over and over down the road bank into mud and weeds. I was so stunned and scared that I staggered to my feet, scampered out of the ditch and just took off running down the road. My father, who was partway out of the car, got back in and drove past me with the faulty door flapping. He stopped the car, jumped out, and tackled me to a stop. He just held me until I stopped shaking. I started to cry. By this time Mom was there, checking the damage. I had skinned my knees, was muddy all over, and my bottom hurt something fierce. Needless to say, Dad did not photograph the light, and no apples were picked that day. I sat cuddled up on Mom's lap all the way home, with my rescued Janice hugged tight.

When we got home, I found enough strength to give the car door a swift kick and yell "stupid door!" The next day, I had a humdinger of a bruise on my hip and scratches all down my left arm. Mercurochrome was painted here and there from my shoulder to my ankles. Dad took the car to the repair shop first thing in the morning for a new lock on the door.

7

SEPTEMBER 1944 — FEVERS

*O*nce again, *I drove the length of Bloomsgrove Avenue, turned right on Hope Street, and drove to Dr. Powers School. Sadly, it was boarded up, and a banner hung haphazardly, announcing "75 Years of Memories."*

The play yard at Dr. Powers Elementary School stretched all across the back end of the school and wrapped around the Hope Street side. The ground was covered with cinders and gravel. Since coal was the main fuel used for heating purposes, cinders were plentiful. The sharp shards made stumbling children easy prey. Most of us had scarred knees embedded with little black specks under the skin. We made a conscious effort to stay on our feet and avoid falling as we flew across the playground in pursuit of peer enemies or when we played Red Rover and Monkey-in-the-Middle. Cinders had pierced right through my cotton rib stockings on numerous occasions, and Mom had to darn them. My stockings always had lumpy woolly blobs at the knees, a testimony that Mom was no expert with a needle.

At recess, classes were segregated into play areas to keep the little ones safe from the bullies and to prevent accidents. The teachers did not want the younger kids to get trampled by crazy boys running after a football. One day, a Grade 8 boy was running backward to catch an airborne ball and he ran right over a first-grader, knocking him to the ground. The little guy was hurt really bad, and the principal and a teacher gathered him up and ran across the road to the hospital. We all stood around and gawked as they disappeared into the side door of the hospital. For the rest of that week, the Grade 1's and 2's got to have their recess at the front of the school where there was grass and sidewalk. That was the week I discovered skipping.

Teachers allowed skipping at the front of the school away from the cinders. It was mostly girls who skipped, and they came and went from school with their ropes slung over their shoulders or skipped all the way home. I joined their ranks with my newly purchased red rope with shiny wooden handles. I saved three allowances and earned money polishing shoes to buy my rope. During morning and afternoon recess, a dedicated group of skippers gathered out in front of Dr. Powers School to test their own skills and each other's ability.

I mastered the single rope in no time and graduated to double dutch, then peppers. I could skip longer than nearly anyone because I almost never tripped the rope. "One, two buckle my shoe, three four, touch the floor, five, six pick up sticks" was my favourite; I could do all the actions and seldom missed a step. Of course you never knew when someone was going to yell "peppers!" and the ropes would fly faster and faster. My braids jumped high and slapped my face on the way down. I constantly scuffed my penny loafers with so much skipping. As soon as I got home after school, I always had to change into my "street" clothes; now I had to polish my shoes as well. I was always open to polishing Dad's shoes, too, because he paid me. I got a nickel if they "shine till you can see your face in 'em," as my dad would say. I could spend that nickel on anything I wanted and I nearly always wanted strawberry licorice twists, my favourite candy, but I spent the last one on the skipping rope. Anyway, skipping soon joined my growing list of "best things."

Lucy had been absent from school for a few days. Someone knocked at the classroom door, and I watched Miss Weldon nodding her head and looking my way with a frown. "Molly," she called. "Will you please go to the office?" When I peered around the corner of the office door, I was surprised to see my mother waiting there, twisting and twisting her best embroidered handkerchief, the one my grandmother in Ireland had sent her for Christmas. She looked really worried, she kept squeezing that hanky and crossing and uncrossing her legs. She looked at me and ran and grabbed me in a big hug as if I were going to evaporate. She held me tight then nodded at the principal, Mr. Bradley, before she spoke to me.

"Molly," she said, tightening her arms around me, "Lucy is very sick — very, very sick. She has a nasty disease called infantile paralysis, also known as polio. That is why she is not in school. She is in the hospital. It is a very serious disease and infectious. That means others can catch it from her, and she might have passed it on to you."

"Will she die?" I asked, scared out of my wits. I looked out the window at the hospital right across the road and I wanted to just race over there and see Lucy. I imagined her being taken in the side door on a stretcher or gathered in her father's arms.

"We pray she will get better, but right now she is a very, very sick little girl. Molly, I want you to listen to me, because she is your best friend and you were always with her. We are worried that you may have been exposed to polio germs. It is very important that others are protected as well. I am taking you home with me; you are being put into quarantine until we are absolutely sure you do not contract the disease and cannot pass it to anyone else."

"Can I go see Lucy?"

"No, she can't have visitors. She is in quarantine, too, but in the hospital. And Molly, this is a very serious matter. You have to stay home and cannot see anyone. Ray and Daddy are going to stay at the Trustlers' house until we know it is safe for them to come home. I was exposed to polio as a child, so I am probably immune. So I will be at home with you."

I stared at Mom in disbelief. Everyone was familiar with quarantines back then. A health official would come by your house and put a red notice on the front door for scarlet fever or a yellow one for measles. I had the measles when I was three and had to stay in a dark room for ages, so now I was immune to measles; Mom said that meant I couldn't catch them again. That's what she meant when she said she was immune to polio. "The incubation time for infantile paralysis is three weeks," explained Mom as the principal nodded.

The house seemed still without Ray's feet racing here and there and without Dad's booming voice. My mother constantly felt my forehead, took my temperature, and worried. She hugged me for no reason, too, really tight, like I might go away or something. I was allowed to go out in the backyard during the day but not the front, and I couldn't have any friends over to play. It took a long time for the days to go by, and I was really bored with nothing to do. There is only so much reading and colouring one can do, and it is no fun playing paper dolls without friends. Mom played fish and Chinese checkers with me and she taught me a few new songs.

FLASH AS A PUPPY

One morning, the second week I was home, Mommy's eye had those little sparkles they got when she was going to tell you something special. She had a way of slipping little smiles at you so her dimples dented and her eyes shone. She kept rubbing her hands along her housedress pockets and peering out the front windows. I asked what was going on but got no answer. The morning went on and she just grinned and patted my head whenever I was close by. I knew something was up.

"Molly," I heard my father's deep voice call. He had started coming home for lunch two days before. Ray still was not allowed to come home. "Come here, I need your help. I left something on the veranda; can you fetch it for me?"

"On the front veranda! Out front?"

"Just outside the door. It will be all right — go ahead."

I skipped down the hall and dove for the heavy front door using all my strength to yank it open. Just as I grabbed for the screen I saw the biggest brown eyes peering at me from a small, blonde, quivering ball of fur cowering in the corner of a cardboard box.

"A puppy! Is he mine?"

"*She* . . . and yes, she is."

I knew right away I would call her "Flash," because I loved her in a flash. Gathering her up, I nuzzled her close and was thanked with a little puppy whimper and a wet cheek where she licked. Quickly, I came to my senses and put her back in the box. "She can't come in! She will get polio!"

"Dogs don't get polio," said Mom, who was standing beside me with a great big smile.

Flash was a golden cocker spaniel and became my constant companion. Her wiggly little fat body was ever ready to be with me, and she slathered kisses all over my face. The two remaining weeks fled by as I played, cuddled, read to, and ran with Flash. Being confined to the house and backyard didn't seem to matter any longer.

Flash made me laugh when she ran after me, lost her balance, and fell into a rolling ball of fur. She yipped with pleasure at the smallest things, tried unsuccessfully to catch a fly buzzing over her head, and her ears flew inside out when she ran. Of course, I had to learn all about training her to do her business outside and teach her not to nip or chew shoes and sofa arms. She was a busy puppy and had no idea she wasn't allowed to get into everything. Her very favourite game was tug of war. Mom found an old piece of flannelette blanket for her to sleep on, but Flash didn't leave it in her bed — she dragged it everywhere. Attempts to take it away resulted in fierce growling and pulling . . . well, as fierce as a nine-week-old puppy can be. Then she would give up and flop down, falling into a deep sleep. I was happy to watch her, with her fat little belly, all cuddled into her "blankie." She was my friend.

The days of quarantine finally passed, and I returned to school, healthy and robust. Ray came home and life returned to normal. My mother wasn't tense anymore and she stopped feeling my forehead every time I passed her. I was a little sorry to leave Flash, but my mother said she needed a rest from me. "She's still a puppy and needs lots and lots of sleep. She can do that while you are at school." I ran all the way to school, my skipping rope slung over my shoulder. I was so happy to get back to class and see my friends. But Lucy wasn't there.

Miss Weldon gathered me tight into her rough tweed jacket and told me how happy she was that I was back. She talked about

Lucy and we coloured pictures and wrote in a lined exercise note-book, a whole one! Usually we had notebooks that were cut in half. A grownup took the book to Lucy at the hospital. In a few weeks, we heard she was being moved to a special kind of hospital where there were lots of patients with polio. I looked over at her empty desk and crossed my fingers that Lucy would get well.

Field Day was new to me, and I listened wide-eyed as the teacher ex-plained how we would compete for ribbons and might win a trophy by participating in sporting activities. Miss Weldon took us out to the playground during class time! At the back of the playground, pits had been dug for jumps, standing broad and running broad. We got to practise and had to learn to put our hands forward instead of behind when we fell or the judge would mark where our hands landed as the distance we had jumped. We got to run around the school and then were divided up into relay teams of four on a team. We ran with a stick and passed it to our team member standing up the road. The fastest team was the winner. I was really excited about Field Day, and at home around the supper table the conversation was all about how Ray and I would compete and in what sports we were most likely to have suc-cess. Every child in every class had to try all the different sports.

"Your father was quite an athlete in his day," Mother inter-jected.

"You were?" questioned Ray. "What sport?"

"Sports," answered Mom. "He still holds the record for cycling in Northern Ireland."

Both Ray and I stared at this man we knew as a policeman, a disciplinarian, a father, but never as an accomplished athlete. We listened, mouths open, as Dad told us that as a young man he had toured Ireland competing as a cyclist, weightlifter, lightweight boxer, and sprinter. He reached into the china cabinet and brought out a little fuzzy box full of medals. It was almost too much to absorb all at once. When he told me he lifted twenty stone just to earn shillings, I thought he went looking for twenty rocks. That is when I learned that there were different measuring systems across the world.

Field Day arrived, and the whole school population marched up Ward Street to the fairgrounds. The area inside the racetrack was marked off into different sports activities. We were told which ones they were, and we had to go to them one by one, classroom by classroom. "Stay together and no straying" were the instructions for the day.

Sports were definitely not my thing. I came in ahead of "Fat" Charlie in the sprint, but he was last. No one chose me for the relay after that. I barely got off the starting board in the broad jump and landed on my rump. I never did get over the bar in the high jump. Everyone had red ribbons, blue ribbons, or yellow ribbons except me—or so it seemed.

At supper, Ray went on and on about the six ribbons he was sporting: three red for first place, one blue for second place and two yellow. Dad and Mom praised him and said how proud they were. I couldn't eat and said I had a tummy ache and left the table. In my room, I scrambled onto my bed and crammed into the corner sniveling into Flash's neck. She licked me anyway; she didn't care that I was a loser. Mom came up and said nice things to try to make me feel better, but there was no way. Nobody could be proud of me. Two days later, my dad arrived home with a second-hand bike, "a little the worse for wear," he said, but sturdy and good to learn on. He gave me pant leg clamps and walked beside me until I stopped wobbling. It didn't take long. It seemed that my skipping rope legs transferred well to the bicycle. My bike became an extension of myself, and in no time I was flying along the roads outracing all my friends. I spent allowance money on a bell that Mr. Dixon screwed onto my handlebars, and he found a wire carrier basket for the front. I tried to put Flash in the basket, but she would have nothing to do with that! I made up my mind that next year I would enter the bicycle race on Field Day.

❋ 8 ❋

PORT HOPE AGRICULTURAL FAIR

*M*any of my childhood memories centred around activities at the fairgrounds. I drove through the gates and gazed at modern structures that no longer looked as my memory had recorded them.

My introduction to the Port Hope Annual Agricultural Fair happened almost as soon as I started Grade 2 at Dr. Powers Public School. Posters showing colourful clowns with big red mouths and prancing horses appeared on telephone poles and in store windows. On October 6th and 7th, the annual Port Hope Agricultural Fair that had been going on every year for a long, long time, like history, was going to be held just up the street from the school at the fairgrounds. There was even going to be a carnival section with rides and games and everything. The kids at school talked and talked about the fair, because there were competitions for school kids, and schools in the town went against each other to compete for prizes.

Miss Weldon announced that our class was going to make a diorama as a class project, and, if it was good enough, she would enter it into the school classroom exhibit at the fair. She explained that a diorama was like a toy model with little miniature figures and buildings, usually a scene or a three-dimensional picture. All the entries were judged by important people in the town like school principals and church ministers. The best ones were pinned with a ribbon: red for first place, blue for second, yellow for third, and white for honourable mention. She told us that this year's theme was "In the Barnyard."

Miss Weldon held up a large piece of board. "Class, this will be the base for the diorama. Now think about a barnyard and what you would see in it and how it should look." Then she asked for ideas.

"It will need to be fenced in. All barnyards have a fence," yelled Wally without waiting to put up his hand.

"Good idea, Wally. But please let's do this in an orderly fashion," Miss Weldon said as she wrote "fence" on the blackboard, then turned and said, "Next."

As she pointed at each of us in turn, the blackboard soon had "fence," "dirt," "grass," "pond," "animals (cows, horses, pigs, chickens, geese, goats, kittens)," "farmer," "wagon outside fence," and "the farm dog."

Miss Weldon then drew a picture on the side blackboard of a barnyard with all the animals and everything we had suggested. We were to assemble the diorama using the picture on the board as our layout plan. We were each to make or find something shown in the barnyard picture.

First we went on an exploring trip around the schoolyard after borrowing a bucket and a shovel from the janitor, Mr. Brown. He had a small pile of dirt left over from gardening, so let us take a shovelful from there. We gathered grass and dried weeds "for fodder." Miss Weldon explained that fodder was another word for food animals ate, like hay. Wally shinnied up a dead tree and broke off two small branches to make the fence.

"Look," yelled Emma, pointing at something in the ditch. "String!"

"That will do for fence wire. Great find, Emma," praised Miss Weldon. "Wally, get down from that tree. This is not playtime." Wally was hanging with his knees from a branch, monkey-style, with his arms dangling toward the ground.

Ronny Graves took to pelting Wally with clumps of dried grass, and before you could say, "Jack's your Uncle," others joined in. Ronny landed one right on Wally's head! Boy, did he let out a yell! Then when Wally went to brush the dirt off his face, he lost his balance and fell to the ground. He wasn't hurt, but getting up, he dove for Ronny, and the next thing we knew, fists were flying and it became a free-for-all. Miss Weldon raised her hand and in a sharp voice commanded everyone to "sit down." Wally, with his mud-streaked cheeks and chin, was the last one to sit and instantly stuck his tongue out at Ronny. Ronny started to get to his feet but Miss Weldon quickly put a stop to that. In a single line we were ushered back to the classroom, with Wally and Ronny right in front of the teacher. When we got back to the room, Ronny was made to sit on a chair, all by himself, in the cloakroom. He was lucky he didn't get the strap!

We set about mixing mucilage into the dirt and packing the mixture onto the board. We were all sticky, but Miss Weldon had thought to bring a dishpan and towels to rinse the mud off our hands. She took the end of one of the towels and rubbed Wally's face clean. Wally was put in charge of building the fence. He cut the branches into sticks all the same length and shoved them into the dirt before the glue dried. The next day, he strung the string between them for fence wire. He even built a gate out of the branches. I offered to make a pig out of Plasticine, and right away others offered to make cows, horses, geese, etc. Miss Weldon gave us each a scrap of paper cut to the size our Plasticine animals should be "to keep them in proportion," she said.

Every afternoon, we worked on the diorama, and the excitement built as the date for the fair drew near. I made my pig three times before I got it the same size as the scrap of paper. We painted an area in the barnyard blue for a pond and sat little yellow clay ducks on it. They looked just like they were floating. We all thought our barnyard was superb. Then one day we came into the classroom and the diorama was gone.

"I took it up to the fairground after school yesterday," explained Miss Weldon. "They are judging the entries this morning and the fair opens to the public this afternoon."

"We have to go to the fair tonight!" I screamed as I rushed through the door after school. "I have to see what we won!"

A steady stream of people was walking up Ward Street toward the fairgrounds, and the lineup at the ticket office was really long. It took way too long to move forward. I kept running back and forth trying to make the line move faster. Finally, we were through the gates, and even the cotton candy booth did not distract me from pulling Mom toward the big red barn where I knew the classroom entries were displayed. Ray wanted to watch the horse races but was firmly told that he was to "stay with us and Molly; don't race ahead and get lost in the crowd."

When I got to the entrance of the red barn, there were several old farmers standing there talking, puffing on pipes, and blocking the way in!

In a polite voice I said, "Excuse me." But they paid no attention and didn't move an inch until Mom gently put her hand on a man's arm and said, "Mr. Skelton, may we get by?"

Then I was off, up and down the aisles until I spied our diorama. A fancy blue ribbon hung on the table beneath it.

"Second place — how wonderful!" exclaimed Mother.

"I wanted to get first," I responded with a pout.

"Let's see. Here's the one that got first — it is really quite similar to yours, but they have real water in the pond and ducks floating in it. Very clever."

"It's not clever at all. It's stupid!"

"Molly, getting first place is not what is important. You have to learn to give credit where credit is due. You all worked together, and so did the class that won. Second place is a wonderful recognition of your efforts. Now show me your pig."

Reluctantly, I pointed at my pig.

"Oh, my! It's beautiful! I am so proud of you. It's a first-class pig!

"Ray, didn't your class place any entries?"

Scuffing his foot in the sawdust, Ray nodded. "We all had to draw barnyard animals. The teacher entered mine."

There were rows and rows of classroom entries, dioramas, papier mâché animals, posters, and all along the walls, pictures and more pictures. On the other side of the barn, there were lots and lots of vegetables, grain, pickles, sewing, and baking. On that side, adults were wandering around talking and nodding, indicating items on the long tables and nodding with approval. On our side, kids were racing between the aisles shouting and pointing. Ray hung back as we searched along the wall. A red ribbon hung beneath a charcoal drawing of a horse's head with perky ears and a full mane. Mother leaned in and read "Ray Carson" on the tag.

"Ray! You got first prize!"

"I know," he said looking from Mom to me.

"Mollikins!" Oh, I hope nobody heard her call me Mollikins. "Aren't you thrilled that your brother won first prize?"

Reluctantly, I nodded, remembering to give credit where it was due. "Next year our class will beat the pants off old Central School. Anyway, I am glad *you* won, Ray. What's your prize?"

"Two dollars."

"Two dollars! Just for an old picture you drew! Holy cow, you can draw yourself rich!"

We wandered around looking at other entries then left the barn as evening approached, with its cooling temperatures and noise and confusion. The cattle barn was right next to the red barn, so we went to see all the animals. It sure stank! I bent down to tie my shoelace, and a cow's tail swatted me right across my head. Boy, did I jump! Ray was laughing to beat the band. Mom had her hand over her mouth as if she were going to burst, then I started giggling, too. We laughed our way through cows, sheep, pigs with little squealing babies, and great big horses — "Percherons," Mother said. I was very careful to stay clear of that tail! I liked the farm animals but I kept pulling Mom's arm to get her to hurry to the midway.

The merry-go-round was grinding out loud, tinny music. Men at booths holding a cigarette in one corner of their mouths shouted out the other: "Three balls for a nickel! Take home a lovely prize for your sweetie!" Kids were screaming as they pulled their parents forward. The loudspeaker at the racetrack could be heard clear across the whole fairground announcing the winners of the last sulky race. Ray, after pleading and promising to behave himself, was finally allowed to go on his own to the track. He ran off to meet his buddies at the railing.

Mom and I wandered over to the circus area. Well, it wasn't really a circus with elephants or anything, but there was a high wire strung between two poles. A man in white tights was way up in the air, walking along the wire and holding a pole. A big net below him stood ready to catch him in case he fell — he wobbled quite a lot and when he did, everyone sucked in their breaths. When he got safely to the other side, he bowed as everyone clapped. Next a beautiful lady wearing a fancy bathing suit with sparkly jewels all over it climbed to the top of another pole. She hooked a long strap to a ring at the top then pushed herself out into space. She spun and twirled, looking ever so beautiful way up there, like jewels dancing in the air. Then she slipped. All I heard was sucked air then everything went real quiet. We watched as she caught her foot in the strap on the way down. She stretched out and blew a kiss to the audience. There were lots of "oohs!" as the crowd let out that sucked-in air. The trapeze lady

(Mom told me that is what she is called) did lots of twirls and som-
ersaults before she lifted her foot from the strap and dove into the
net, bounced up, and stood in the middle with her arms raised. The
audience went wild. I joined in, jumping up and down, excited and
amazed at the daring feats I had just seen.

Mom and I rode the merry-go-round. She lifted me onto a big
white horse with a golden saddle then got on a brown horse with red
reins prancing beside mine. After our trusty steeds came to a halt,
we strolled down the midway, bought cotton candy, and watched
people throw horseshoes at bottles. The smell of taffy apples, horse
manure, sweaty people, and ladies' perfume wafted on soft, warm
breezes as we walked along the dusty path. We laughed at the antics
of a silly clown that kept trying to wipe the dirt off everyone's shoes
and we waved to Dad as he was directing traffic in his chief-of-police
uniform. Patti, with her mom and dad, caught up to us and she and
I got to go for a ride in a goat cart. We sat in the cutest little wagon
and held the reins all by ourselves. The goat seemed to know exactly
when to take us back to the get-off point. The owner let us give her a
special candy and a pat for being a "good girl."

We all joined Ray and Dougy at the railing near the racetrack
to watch the horses pull a funny little cart with a man lying on his
back — sulky racing, it was called. Dougy knew one of the drivers,
Dan Sturges, and pointed to #11, the cart he was driving. We all
shouted and wanted #11 to win. The dust was so thick when they
went past us, I couldn't see anything, but I felt the horses' hooves
thumping the ground so hard it sent ripples right through my feet.

"What happened? Who won?" I screamed over the noise of
cheering men and women.

"Don't know," said Dougy, "but Dan was close. Let's listen to the
results."

A man was standing on a tall platform with a loud-hailer and
announced the results. Dan came in second. Everyone talked about
what a great thing it was to place second. I thought about our diorama and began to realize "second" wasn't so bad after all.

I was too scared to go on the Ferris wheel, but Mom and I
watched Ray and Dougy go way up in the air strapped into a flimsy
open bench with only a metal bar across their laps to hold them in.
They plunged down with lots of screeching by the girls and laughter

from the boys. Mom squeezed my hand so hard it hurt and she didn't let up until Ray and Doug were safely on the ground.

With promises of a return visit, we left the fairgrounds. Walking home, we could hear the festive noises getting fainter and fainter as we got farther away. The fair was on for the next two days, but only in the daylight hours, because of the blackout orders, but the days were still long in October. We went again with Grandma and Uncle Bill on Saturday afternoon. My uncle — remember he was a pilot in the air force — was home on leave, so he and Grandma came for a visit all the way from Toronto.

Of course I dragged them into the red barn to see Ray's horse and my class's diorama. They thought my pig was first-rate. Uncle Bill bought me more cotton candy and he won a stuffed animal at the shooting gallery.

"What animal do you want?" he asked.

Right there in the front row was a smiling pink pig.

9

GOBLINS AND SUCH

I walked toward the old brownstone across the street from #19. It would now be considered a heritage home, majestic and true to turn-of-the century design. The veranda was gone! I remembered pushing the doorbell that first Halloween on Bloomsgrove Avenue.

I got a really mean, nasty cold, probably because I got my feet all wet from stomping on the crusty ice that was forming on puddles. I can never walk by that thin ice — I just have to tap it with my toe to see how strong it is. If it is too thick to break with a toe tap, a good whomp! with my heel usually shatters the ice, and the cold water rushes over my shoe before I can pull it away. Ray can get his foot away in time, but I never can. Anyway, I got soaked walking home from school and woke up the next morning with a stuffed head and a runny nose. Mom put her hand on my forehead, "Mollikins, you are staying home today."

"No!" I screamed. "We are decorating the classroom for Halloween and I made a beautiful witch that I want Miss Weldon to put up!"

"Well, it will just have to wait. You have a little fever, and if you want to get better by Halloween night, we'd better keep you warm and cozy."

Well, that was that! By mid-afternoon, I was coughing and sneezing like anything. In the middle of the night, I woke up barking like a seal. The next thing I knew, Mom was standing over me with a stern look and felt my forehead again. "Hmm, we will have to do something about that bark," she said. "It's deep," and left the room. She came back and huddled me in my blanket and marched me to the kitchen. A honey bucket was steaming on the stove.

"Oh, no! I hate this," I winced. That look mothers can give made me succumb, and before I knew it I was standing on a kitchen chair.

A towel was draped over my bent head and hung over the steaming honey bucket to direct the steam up my nose. The mentholated fumes tore at the back of my throat and burned the inside of my chest. I choked and sputtered as my tears rolled into the steamy mixture.

"There, just breathe in one more time, before taking a rest," Mom cooed.

Regular doses of this torture helped my breathing, and my cough eased. Mom rubbed mentholated oil my chest and put me back to bed. The next morning, the nasty business was repeated. The smell of menthol stunk up the whole kitchen and me for days. I missed two days of school and I still smelled, but Miss Weldon hung my witch anyway. The cold gave way to Mother's doctoring, and I was well enough by Halloween to go trick-or-treating.

Mom tied an old sheet around me and cut holes for me to see where I was walking. I was supposed to be a ghost, but I knew I was just a seven-year-old kid in a sheet! Ray had already disappeared, dressed as a pirate with a drawn-on mustache. He had run off to meet Dougy and to get the "best loot" before it was all gone. Dougy knew all the best houses and he and Ray didn't need a parent. They got to go *all* the way up and down Bloomsgrove Avenue. *I* had to go with Mom. Patti's dad was not well, and her mother had to mind their door, so Patti came with us. Patti was dressed as an Arabian princess with real see-through harem pants and a vest with sparkling jewels. Her father brought them home from the Middle East, wherever that is. Her belt had little bells that tinkled whenever she moved and she had a vest with jewels that sparkled and shone. She looked just like a fairytale princess. I wished my dad had gone to the Middle East.

Bloomsgrove Avenue was alive with excited kids dressed in all sorts of get-ups. Several grown-ups were in costume, too. Patti and I waved at some Indians and a hobo we knew and we yelled across the street at two clowns from my class. Some were carrying brown paper bags, some had baskets, and some had pillowcases. Mom was quick to express how she was not impressed with that kind of greed. Patti and I carried honey buckets, ones that did not smell like menthol. We had had an early supper and got out on the street before it was dark because, Mom said, "in wartime the street lights cannot be on." Dogs were barking and barking with all the commotion.

Rushing ahead of Mom, Patti and I chattered about the best loot strategy and decided we wanted to go to the "rich" houses first. The Ranciers, who lived in the brownstone across the street, worked long hours, and we had yet to meet them. Patti and I urged Mom to go there first, sure that this was the house with the best pickings. That was a definite mistake. It became a "getting to know you" visit for Mom and the Ranciers. Patti and I clutched our honey buckets and paced the end of the long veranda, swung on the cream-coloured pillars, and ate our licorice pipes.

For what seemed hours there was talk of the war again and finally polite goodbyes. We just knew that all the candy at the other houses would be gone by this time. Racing ahead of Mom, we went to two other houses on that side of the street, delighted to find they still had candy, then we crossed to the other duplex like ours (there were only two on the street). The door was answered by a man wearing a light-brown army uniform and high black boots. He looked a little weird, with a stiff black mustache, dark, piercing eyes, and his hair plastered across his forehead. He raised his arm and greeted us with "*Heil*!" Something about him gave me the creeps, and I hated those hard little spicy candies he handed out. Next we went to the house where the biker lived, and they had the best treats: caramel apples! Surprisingly, we filled our buckets from just ten houses. We had bubble gum, jujubes, licorice, and, best of all, lots and lots of jelly beans. The red ones were my favourites.

The next evening, we went to a movie at the Capitol Theatre. We hardly ever went to a nighttime movie, only matinees on Saturday, so this was a very rare treat. I can't remember what movie it was, but there was lots of singing and dancing, and Mom made fun of Dad's getting too much of Rita Hayworth's legs. Well, she did have lots of scenes with them showing, with her skirts slit up the side, and she lifted them right up when she danced! At the night movies, they show newsreels before the main feature; at the matinees, they showed cartoons. I preferred cartoons. The news was really boring stuff all about the war, but we had to sit quietly through it anyway. A man called Hitler was shouting at a big crowd, and everyone in the crowd raised their arms and yelled, "*Heil Hitler*!" I grabbed at Mom's sleeve. "There's the man from last night, you know the one, at the other duplex, the creepy guy that gave out the candies I didn't like. That's him!"

"Hush, Molly, that's not him. The man at the duplex was just pretending to be Hitler. That was his costume for Halloween. Not a very tasteful choice, considering," she said.

Well, I knew he *was* Hitler; he was right there in front of me, handing out hard little candies. I saw him with my own eyes. If we had not gone to the night show that special evening, I would never have known that Hitler lived on our street.

When we lived in Huntsville we paid for matinee movies with balls of string or rolled-up balls of silver foil from cigarette packages. It was to support the war effort, I was told. I didn't care about that, all I knew was, we had marks on the kitchen counter to measure if the balls were large enough to pay for a movie: a smaller one for foil and a larger one for string. They had to be tight, too. "No messing around with loose balls," the creepy old man ticket-taker would always say with a sleazy chuckle, reaching over to pat my head. I always tried to duck clear before he touched me. At the Port Hope theatre, they took only money: five cents for a single feature, ten cents for a double. Every Saturday afternoon, there was a matinee attended by children only, except for a boy called Trevor, whose mother always brought him in a wheelchair.

Leo was one of the toughest guys in the neighbourhood. He even spat in the street! I watched his mother smack the back of her hand across his head when she didn't like something he had done, and he never cried. I once asked him if it hurt, because my parents never hit us. "Naw," he said, but I didn't believe him. That's why I was surprised when I looked out the front window the very next afternoon after we saw the Rita Hayworth movie and saw Leo sitting on the curb, crying. I turned from the window yelling at the top of my lungs about my delicious observation. "Bawl-baby Leo is sitting on the curb crying like a wimp!"

A pair of commanding hands, one clamped firmly across my mouth and the other grasping my upper arm dragged me away from in front of the living room window down the hall to mid-kitchen. With a toss of her head, Mom motioned Ray, who was sitting at the dining room table sorting hockey cards, to join us. My mother's soft tones hushed me with a finger to her lips. She grabbed the hairbrush to begin the job of plaiting my long, dark hair (Mom always had to brush my hair when there were important issues to be discussed). She told us in a very sad voice that Leo's dad had been killed in the war, shot down in the trenches. This was a puzzle to me. Patiently mother explained that war was a very nasty business, and many good people got killed trying to make the world a better place and save it from tyrants like Hitler.

"You mean Hitler killed Leo's father?" I asked with astonishment.

"Well, sort of," she replied. "You see, he has many, many soldiers working for him, and they do all the killing."

I felt really, really bad for Leo, but I couldn't wait for my hair to be finished so I could run to Patti with this news. Hitler lived right down the street and he had killed Leo's father. Boy, it would not be long before my daddy would arrest him! We sat on our front steps, picking at the peeling paint that was supposed to be dark green but was coated in a milky white powdery stuff, and talked about it all day. We kept a close watch for my dad to come with the police car and drag that Hitler guy away. Patti and I shared our news with Donna and Becky and even got brave enough to walk by the "Hitler duplex." We strained to peek in the windows, but the blinds were drawn. "Betcha he is hiding so as not to get caught." Later in the day, we saw Leo coming out his driveway kicking stones, head down and looking very sad. "Don't worry," I yelled. "My father will arrest that nasty Hitler."

The police car didn't come, and I never quite understood why I was sent to my room with a strong warning to stop spreading tall tales and causing so much trouble when our poor neighbours were dealing with such a dreadful loss.

✳ 10 ✳

PETS AND THINGS

*S*trolling *along Bloomsgrove Avenue, I spied two little girls playing with a kitten on the lawn. They teased it with a bit of paper tied on the end of a string. It reminded me of Ray's and my pets.*

Ray had a paper route and earned lots and lots of money; he didn't even need to ask when he wanted to buy licorice. But you'll never believe what he did buy! He bought a rat! And this was the guy who made fun of me keeping fuzzy-bear caterpillars in a box in my room. A rat!

Pesky lived in a cage in Ray's room. Pesky did not like me, and I did not like his little sharp teeth or his skinny pink tail. He was mostly white but he didn't have much hair on his tail or his ears, so they looked pink. Ray tried to tell me that Pesky was not related to the rats that got in garbage or lived at the dump. "He is a domestic rat, raised to be a pet." He was still a creepy rat as far as I was concerned. Ray and he got along fine, though, and they were often sprawled out together on Ray's bed, Ray reading, Pesky munching on cheese or lettuce. He had little sharp eyes that watched me whenever I was near. I knew he was just looking for the moment he could take a nip at my finger. I wanted to pinch his pink ears.

Pesky was not allowed out of Ray's room for fear that Flash or Marmalade might harm him. Mom was always on at Ray about his responsibilities. He had to make sure that Pesky was locked safely in his cage when he was not playing with him. Pesky had a big cage with a ramp and a wheel he could run along inside of and make it turn. Ray was not very careful and often forgot to put Pesky back in his cage or lock the door. I think he would just forget that Pesky was asleep in a drawer or snuggled under the covers. Mom was forever rounding Pesky up and tucking him in the cage herself, with a "one of these days" as she closed the door. Ray always got a scolding when that happened and received a warning: "Either look after Pesky or he has to go." Pesky got his name because he was a bit ornery and did not always co-operate as he should — like come when he was called.

Mom played bridge. That's a card game that needs four women to get together one day every week. They go to one house one week and to another the next week, taking turns. The hostess — that's what Mom called the one who held the game at her house — has to have a card table and cards and to serve tea and fancy little cakes called petty fours, covered all over with icing and fancy designs. Mom got them at the bakery. I loved going to the bakery with Mom because they always gave me a sugar cookie with coloured sugar stuck on the top. When the card game was at our house, I always helped set out the best china cups and saucers, and Mom let me have one petty four for doing that. Mom explained that petty fours were little bite-size cakes and the name was spelled petits fours. *Petits* was "little" in French, and a piece of cake was cut into four portions, so the name was a mixture of French and English.

When we got ready for one of those bridge games, Mom even set out the little silver coffee spoons, rubbed with the rose cloth until they gleamed, and fancy starched linen napkins; nothing but the best for these ladies. Patti's mom, Mrs. Miller, came. I didn't know the other two, but Mom said Mrs. Miller was a good partner. That meant Mom liked to play on her team.

One time when it was Mom's turn to be the hostess, Pesky was not in his cage, and Mom couldn't find him anywhere. When Ray and I came home from school for lunch, Mom was in a state.

"You had better find that rat or pay the consequences," she snarled at Ray. We set about looking everywhere. Ray and I scoured his bedroom, looking under his bed, in his closet, and in his desk drawers, with no luck. Then we searched my room and checked the house from top to bottom — no Pesky. We set off for school for the afternoon leaving my mother with hands firmly clamped on her hips and lips drawn into a tight line. After school, we returned just as the ladies were waving goodbye. I saw Mother give Ray a poisonous "you're in trouble" look.

"Do you know where Pesky is?" She hissed at Ray as she smiled and waved goodbye to the bridge ladies now at the sidewalk. Turning sharply on her heel, she grasped Ray by his collar. "Come here and I will show you!"

Ray and I followed Mom into the living room, stepping around the bridge chairs and table now strewn with dirty dishes and messy napkins. Mom steered Ray to the front of the flowered sofa facing the window and pointed. "There!" Mom exclaimed shrilly. "The whole afternoon was a disaster! I was so terrified Pesky would wake up and my club members would run screaming — "

Sound asleep in a swag of the white ruffled curtains was a small, solid blob that blended right in.

Ray stepped onto the sofa and gathered the sleeping Pesky from his comfortable hammock. Pesky opened his eyes and looked about as if to say, "What is all the fuss about?" Ray looked at me with a silly smirk and I started to giggle.

"Couldn't you imagine just how frightened poor Pesky would be with all those women screaming all around him?" laughed Ray. "Imagine the poor wee thing running terrified up one of those old crow's stockings, trying to hide in her skirts, only to get stuck in her garters?"

Well, that set us off. Pretend Pesky scenarios abounded. "The poor thing would probably race onto the table and spill the cream then jump onto someone's head." The stories got sillier and the giggles spread. Mom lost it and joined in, and the three of us collapsed on the sofa with tears running down our faces, laughing like fools. Pesky was tucked into Ray's neck as if he didn't have a care in the world. Retelling the story to Dad at supper just sent us into convulsive laughter again.

Shortly after that, Pesky disappeared for good. I overheard Mom and Dad talking, saying that Marmalade was suspect. Several weeks after that, Patches came to live with us.

Dad, as part of his police duties, often stopped in to check on an old man who lived by himself. This day he found the old fellow's family in the process of moving him to Golden Plough Lodge, the end-of-your-life senior's home. They were perplexed about what to do with the old man's pet rabbit. Dad solved that.

Patches was a black and white angora rabbit with the wiggliest nose in the whole world. She loved people and was always up for a cuddle and having her ears gently tugged. She was a year old, so was fully grown and litter trained. Marmalade took one look at this intruder, took a swift swipe at Patches' ears, stalked her and did everything to tell us and Patches that he was not too pleased to have a rabbit in *his* house. Flash took to Patches right away. She just gave Patches a good sniff all over, learned very quickly that you do not sniff rabbits in certain places, and accepted our new family member. Eventually they all came to some kind of agreement with each other and became occasional playmates. It was not uncommon to be sprawled out on the living room carpet with Flash Gordon comics spread about when all of a sudden Patches would rip by, followed by Flash and Marmalade. They would have a great game racing through the dining room, the kitchen, down the hall, through the living room, and round again for about three rounds. Then, without any reason, Patches would flop down, feet splayed behind her, and the race would end. Marmalade would wander off to find a warm snooze spot, and Flash would settle to licking disgusting parts of herself.

Whenever the cat or dog got a bit rough with Patches, she would give them a little nip with her sharp teeth and they soon learned what was and was not acceptable to a rabbit. Patches had the run of the house and learned to come when she was called. She had a little temper and when she wanted attention she would come up beside me and thump a hind foot or tug at my pant legs. She loved to have the bridge of her nose rubbed and was always snuggled under my chin butted up to Flash when we listened to the radio shows. Because she was angora, she had long fur, and I had to brush her every day; just so Flash wouldn't get jealous, I brushed her, too.

Marmalade seemed to lick himself constantly and didn't need brushing. Mom made a little harness for Patches out of a kerchief and a leash out of a long pink ribbon so I could take her into the backyard, where she could munch on fresh grass. I always had to be with her — she was never allowed out alone. She and I communicated through little "hmph-hmph's" and foot-stomping.

Patches would come when called and was more like a cat than a rabbit. Her soft black fur had two white patches; that's how she got her name. Her little fur-covered nose twitched like crazy. Patches knew how to play her audience and when she suspected that the one she was being stroked by was paying less attention to her than she wanted, she would kick her feet, do a few little run-arounds, then promptly go to another person for attention.

One Saturday morning, I came downstairs and could not find Patches anywhere. I called and called. "She's just tucked in somewhere," Mom assured me. As the day wore on, we all became concerned when Patches had not appeared. She was far too social to hide that way. We went searching. We looked in closets, cupboards, the coal bin, and under everything. Flash seemed to understand that something was wrong and stuck her nose into every place we were looking and sniffed and sniffed. The day slipped away without any success. Mom tucked me into bed that night with reassurances. "Don't worry, she is just hiding somewhere. Sometimes when animals have a little tummy ache or are not feeling well they just want to be by themselves. She will likely be back in the kitchen thumping her feet for attention in the morning."

She wasn't. We looked all day Sunday, too. I was in tears, absolutely wretched. My parents came to the conclusion that someone must have accidentally left the back door ajar and she had wandered out. I screamed at my brother, accusing him, and was about to claw him to bits when mother convinced me that that would not solve anything, and we needed Ray to help search. The search moved out of doors. Patches always made her funny little "hmf-hmf" sound and would answer to our call; but no "hmf-hmf" sounds were returned that day. We checked every corner of the garage and looked under it. We searched through the bushes and peered down the street culverts. We alerted the neighbours, but nobody had seen Patches. They all promised to "keep an eye out." I was devastated and frantic to find my special little bunny. I refused to go to school the next day, or the next; I had to find Patches. I wandered from room to room, in the backyard, under the front veranda, and in the neighbours' yards. Mom tried to make me feel better, but I knew she was upset, too.

"Molly," Mom said with her arms around me, "I am afraid we have lost our dear little bunny forever."

"No!" I screamed, refusing to let her touch me as I spun away. "I will find her!"

"Molly, you simply have to understand. Sometimes things just happen. I am sure Patches has found a bunny friend and set up house elsewhere." She tried to console me with hugs and snuggles, but I wanted none of that.

Every time I went into a room, I called Patches. On day four, I was ordered to get ready to go to school. Reluctantly I dressed and, armed with my dirty laundry, I headed down to the basement. Of course I called Patches' name; I hadn't stopped in four days.

And then, I heard "hmf-hmf"! It was very faint, but I was sure I heard it! I called again. Sure enough, the sound was coming from behind the furnace. I looked. No Patches.

"Mom!" I hollered. "I heard her! I heard her!" I raced up the stairs and grabbed Mom's apron to drag her back to the basement with me.

"Now, honeybun, I am sure you *wished* you heard her, but I doubt it," Mom soothed as she followed me to the basement and behind the furnace. We both looked — no rabbit; we listened — no sound.

Mom left the basement shaking her head, but I stubbornly stayed, calling and calling. There it was again! "Mom!" I screamed at the top of my lungs. "I heard her again!"

Before I knew it, Mom was at my side, listening. We were very quiet. There it was again, coming from behind the wall!

"Oh, my goodness," was all mother said as she lunged for a metal thing on the wall (I learned later it was the fireplace cleanout), removed the steel plate, and retrieved a very sad-looking, ash-covered rabbit. Mother handed Patches to me, not even caring that I had my good go-to-school clothes on. I could feel Patches' little heart racing so fast and her eyes darted here and there, afraid to lock onto anything. I cried and cuddled her and cried some more. Ashes were getting up my nose and all over my clothes and face, smudged with my happy tears. There were tears in Mom's eyes, too. "Oh, Molly dear, I am so glad you did not give up."

The night before Patches went missing, Dad had cleaned the fireplace. The red brick fireplace was in the living room and had a cleanout chute at the back. Dad would remove the grate and sweep the ashes down the hole to the chute to be removed from the basement end at a later date. This was not a daily chore; he did it only every month or so in the winter, and the chute in the basement was only cleared a couple of times a year. During this cleaning chore, Dad must have left the room while the cover was off the chute. Being a rabbit, Patches thought she had found her kind of place and went happily down the hole. It was fortunate that it was the first cleaning of the year, and the chute was not very full, and that Patches was so well fed. She was very, very thirsty and very, very dirty when she was rescued.

Patches had to be washed after her ill-fated adventure. Now, washing a rabbit is not something one does every day, and that is a good thing. Mom filled the kitchen sink with warm water and it took both Mom and me to handle that angry little wriggling bundle of wet fur. We had only hair shampoo, and Patches took exception to both the water and the shampoo. Her flailing hind feet sent water all over the kitchen. Not only did we have a wet rabbit, but Mother and I got sopping, too. We did manage to get her washed and most of the soap rinsed out. Wrapped in a big yellow towel, she snuggled close to my chest and settled down into an exhausted sleep. I crooned and held her for a very long time.

Flash watched the whole process and would not leave our wet bunny's side once she was out of the water. She gave Patches the odd caressing lick or two every now and again. Marmalade could not have cared less and snoozed on the window ledge. When I finally did set Patches down on the linoleum, Mom and I broke into fits of laughter, watching the most bedraggled-looking creature you ever saw. Patches just stood there for a few minutes to think about her situation, made a feeble effort to do something about her wet fur, then in disgust she gave up and went right to her bed behind the kitchen stove and slept and slept. "You never saw such a sight in your life," Mom told Dad over the phone.

Patches lived to be eight years old. She never went down a hole again, and, of course, Dad never left the fireplace cleanout cover off again, either.

❋ 11 ❋

FATHER AND DAUGHTER

The old rink is no longer there; it is now a small playground. But I remember the commanding presence of that old metal-sheeted building that stood square and ugly, grey on the outside, a contrast to the colourful activity inside. We used to sneak in the side door to watch hockey games and lacrosse.

"Let's sneak in and watch the hockey game," I heard Ray whisper to Dougy. Eager to be a part of this risky, law-breaking activity, I tagged along.

"What if we get caught sneaking in?" I muttered, fearing my father's reprisal.

"No sissies allowed. Either you stay with us or get on home," Ray announced. Of course I tagged along, with my heart hammering against my ribs. Once safely inside, we sauntered along behind the seats and wedged into a space along the boards between two jack-shirted teenagers. The one beside me smoked and shouted between puffs, grinding out one butt with the heel of his running shoes before he lit another.

The skating rink stood one block back of us, between our house and the school, and was the centre of activity for sports year round. There were hockey games nearly every Saturday night in the winter, and lacrosse and other special events in the summer.

We left the game after the first period and to our surprise when we got home, Mom lit into us. "Have you been over at the rink? You know it is wrong to sneak in. Other people have to pay good money to see hockey, and you little scallywags just think you are entitled to sneak in a back door. Ray, you go to your room and stay there. No *Shadow* for you tonight. Imagine showing your little sister how to be so bad! Molly, you come with me." How did she know where we had been? The answer came when I was snivelling in the bathtub as Mom aggressively scrubbed my smoke-saturated hair.

My father's favourite sport was boxing. "Remember, I used to box in my younger years," he reminded us. He would show Ray and me the finer points of fending off an opponent's punch. "Raise your elbows. That's it." But he didn't take me to a boxing match — he took me to a wrestling match.

"Bill, don't forget you have to look after Molly Saturday night, as Ray and I are going to the indoctrination meeting for the winter Boy Scout camp," I heard Mom telling Dad.

"Jo, that's impossible. Can't you take her with you? Dick Rice and I are going to the wrestling match."

"Bill, how could you forget? You knew this was arranged weeks ago."

"Nuts . . . well, I guess she can come along with us."

"You are not taking a seven-year-old girl to a wrestling match!" My mother's voice was sharp and alarmed.

"Why not? Nothing will happen to her, and I think she will get a kick out of it. Besides, this is an opportunity for her to learn that life is not all about tea parties and dressing up," my father retorted, giving me a wink. Mom's grey eyes shot right through Dad, but he just stood there with a silly smile on his face. With a shrug, Mom backed off. I don't think she had a choice, and Dad knew it. I couldn't wait to go to something that Mom was so miffed about.

Full of curiosity and somewhat nervous, I held tight to Dad's hand as we entered the dark arena. The crowd was nearly all men, and I felt really, really little, looking way up to try and see faces. Most times, I just saw belt buckles and flabby bellies. I didn't know anyone. When we got past the entrance and ticket lobby, hardly a soul was in the bleachers. They were all crowded around a square stage with ropes strung along the sides. Mr. Rice, Dad's friend, waved to us and pointed to seats beside him near the ropes. I could see a big gold ring sparkling on his finger as he waved. When we reached Mr. Rice, I was fascinated to see a thick cigar that was clamped in the side of his mouth. He managed to hold it there while he talked, switching it from side to side. I watched, expecting it to fall out. It didn't.

"Hey, Chief," he greeted. "Well, who might this little cutie be? Could this be Molly?" Without waiting for an answer, he chucked me under the chin and lifted me up. He smelled of Aqua Velva and cigars. "You just set right up here," he sputtered through the cigar and placed me onto a chair. "In fact, if you stay standing on the seat, you will have the best view in the house."

Now that was a strange statement; we were not in a house at all! He was right, though — standing there, I could see over the heads of all the people in front of us (we were only four rows back from the ropes). A bald head was right in front of me, a fuzzy grey one in front of that, and a dark, greasy one plastered down with Brylcreem was in the front seat. Over them, I watched the activity going on around the stage. A tall, thin man leaned over the ropes and spoke with another man, who was wearing a towel around his neck. He nodded, then walked to the opposite corner and spoke with another towel-draped man. He then went to the ropes near the centre, where two men sat at a table outside the stage area. They had a big red bell like the one on the wall of the fire hall. One of them held up a round, very big watch. I leaned into Dad and asked him what was happening. He explained that the roped-off area was called a ring, and the man walking about was the referee; the towel-necked men were trainers, and the man with the watch was the timer.

"The trainers with the towels look after the wrestlers, the referee will count out the falls and call the points, and the men at the table keep score," he explained as he patted my hand and turned to greet someone who had yelled, "Hey, Chief, hows't going?"

"Larry! Good, and how are things with you? Should be a good match! My money's on Fierce Fred. The Mad Marvel is beginning to show his age."

I saw Dad shake hands with Larry, and somehow, when they stopped shaking, Larry had money in his hand, which he quickly put in his pocket. Dad leaned over and whispered that it would not look good if the chief of police placed a bet, so Larry was doing it for him. Now, bets were something I knew a little about. It was all about winning. So this wrestling thing had to be some kind of game. This was the first time I realized that money had anything to do with placing bets; at home, we always wagered dried peas.

I wrinkled my nose as Larry brushed past me in a messy, dark, striped suit and a dirty white shirt; his tie had greasy spots all over it and hung loose. He smoked a cigar too, but it just stayed in one place and he took it out when he talked. I watched him work his way to the back of the crowd, his broad shoulders twisting and turning as he passed rows and rows of mostly men. He often reached across and shook hands, smiled, and nodded before putting something in his pocket. I guessed he was gathering betting money from other people, too.

This was not anything like when Mom took us to a play and there were mostly women in the audience, and we all had to sit quietly and mind our manners. This place was noisy, and everybody was jabbing someone to get his attention or whistling sharp and waving. Nobody was just sitting in their seats. As I watched Larry work his way to the back of the crowd, bright spots flared red as cigarettes were sucked on and faces disappeared in clouds of smoke. I knew I was headed for the bathtub again when Mom got a whiff of me.

Larry reached the bleachers, and I saw him reach over and hand money to another man wearing a Maple Leafs jacket, and he handed Larry some pieces of paper. Larry tucked these pieces of paper between each of his fingers. A very fat woman went up to the Maple Leaf man and handed him more money and she got a piece of paper, too. The only time I had ever seen money exchanged for a piece of paper was when we were going to a movie or a play, but Dad had already paid at the front door. I thought about this as I watched the fat lady waddle away like a turquoise duck, pushing through the crowd and shoving big men aside until she plopped into a ringside seat.

"Folks!" a voice summoned, and everyone stopped talking and turned around to face the ring, where the referee was talking into a microphone. The sound system screeched and everyone laughed. "Tonight you will witness two of the most ferocious wrestlers of all time as they contend for the Eastern title. This is the match of the century! Two mighty men, Fierce Fred and Mad Marvel, right here at Port Hope Arena. Now, put your hands together to welcome the Mad Marvel!"

There was a blast of loud music, the bell sounded, and everyone started shouting and clapping. The next thing I knew, this fancy-looking man was running down the aisle to the stage. He was dressed in the most beautiful shiny outfit I had ever seen, better even than Superman. He stopped and raised his shimmering, bright-yellow cape high over his head. He had tattoos all down his arms and wore skinny tight shorts with stars all over them and a big, black belt. He looked just like a live comic book character. He was the most beautiful man I had ever seen until the referee announced Fierce Fred. Blowing kisses to the crowd, Fierce Fred slowly approached the front, a vision in red. His flaming hair was the same colour as his cape, and he wore high red boots. A silver buckle studded with diamonds sparkled at the waist of his little shorts.

"Daddy, are these real superheroes? Like in the comic books? Can they fly?"

Dad and Mr. Rice exchanged looks and smiled. Mr. Rice patted my head and said, "You just watch, little girlie. These fellows are the wrestlers. They go into the ring and fight."

Fight? Now I was confused. "Which one is the bad guy?" I asked.

"Well my bet's on Fierce Fred, but it could be a close match," my father answered, clapping his hands as the two supermen entered the ring.

I watched as they met in the middle and shook hands, then each went to a little stool set in opposite corners. The men with the towels undid the wrestlers' capes and fussed over them. The bell rang. Well, who would have believed it? Those grown-up men charged across the ring and grabbed at each other, pushing and grappling like silly kids! They were sneering and calling each other names, worse than Wally and Ronny. Mad Marvel threw Fierce Fred to the floor and jumped right on top of him. Everyone roared and screamed. I heard words I knew I was never supposed to hear! The bell rang, and I nearly fell off the chair, it was so loud.

It seemed everyone was puffing on a cigarette or a cigar. Through the smoky haze, I had watched two men grapple and roar and shake their fists and yell vulgar things to the crowd. When the first bell rang, they stopped grappling each other, and Mad Marvel strutted around the ring, growling, with his arms in the air. I just couldn't believe what I was seeing!

That fat old lady in the turquoise dress was jumping up and down shaking her fist and yelling really bad words. Dad told me to pay no mind — it was all in fun. It sure was a different kind of fun. I saw other people shaking their fists at Mad Marvel and booing. Dad said they didn't agree with the referee's ruling.

Then the bell went off again, and before I knew it, Fierce Fred grabbed Mad Marvel from behind by his silver belt, pulled him in tight, lifted him off the ground, and threw him right across the ring. Well, now I knew why Mad was called Mad. He roared just like a lion and charged at Fierce Fred. I watched dumbstruck as shiny bodies writhed and tumbled, stopping only when the bell rang. Then the men with towels around their necks jumped over the ropes and wiped down the sweaty wrestlers, talking at them the whole time before the bell sounded again, at which point the two towel guys jumped out of the ring, and the wrestlers ran at each other again. The crowd was screaming and yelling and smoking. I yelled, too. The bell sounded again, and Dad explained that each time the bell sounded and the wrestlers went to sit in the corner, it was called a round. The wrestlers had to go ten rounds.

Pretty soon the referee grabbed the arm of Fierce Red and held it way up in the air. Everyone clapped. The match was over. Lots of people threw paper up in the air and they didn't seem happy. When we were leaving, the man called Larry slid onto the edge of my seat beside Dad, and I saw him put money in Dad's pocket. "Good choice, Chief," he said. "Paid three to one." I saw Dad smile and nod.

"Bill, you both reek of cigars." Mom didn't want to hear a thing about the wrestling match, but I was so full of it I just couldn't stop babbling. "Shush, Molly, I've heard enough," she snarled as she marched me to the bathtub. I screeched and cried when the shampoo got in my eyes and was only met with, "Well, keep them shut, then." I guess I smelled really bad, because Mom sprayed a little Lily-of-the Valley cologne in my hair and with a wrinkled nose gathered my clothes into a bundle before marching them right down to the washing machine.

I told and retold how those comic book characters threw each other around. My friends were ever so envious, but my mother was much less enthusiastic. Ray was jealous as sin that he'd had to sit through a boring old meeting about sleeping in tents while I went to see the fight of the year with Mad Marvel and Fierce Fred.

✻ 12 ✻

WINTER

I pointed my old Buick toward the bottom of town, heading to Lake Ontario. Just before the lake, I cut to the right and turned in to the railway station. The station house is still there, but the mountains of coal that used to line the sides of the track are gone.

I was jarred awake by a rumbling noise and toys rattling on my windowsill. Terrified, I rushed screaming down the stairs and headlong into the kitchen to my mother's arms.

"Don't be frightened," she cooed. "It's just the coal truck. Winter is coming, and we have to fill the coal bin. I know it is noisy, but nothing to be frightened about."

Still shaking, but now curious, I stood on tiptoe and peered out the dining room window to watch the coal sliding from the tilted truck hopper down a metal chute into the side of the house. The coal bin chute was directly below my bedroom window; that is why it was so loud. Wiping the steamed-up window off with my elbow, I peered out. I couldn't see all the way into the dump truck bed because the sides were boarded up too high. I could see the top of a very sooty man steadily moving black shiny lumps. They tumbled in a steady stream out of an opening at the back of the truck then down the chute into our coal bin. When it was full, the man, black from head to toe, lifted the metal ramp and secured it to the truck with a chain. He climbed into the cab for a few minutes before getting out of the truck and coming to the door. I gasped at the dirt of him and could not believe how the only pink thing I could see was his mouth, which was now saying, "Here's your bill, Ma'am." And that was that; Mom closed the door and returned to her ironing.

I pondered the whole coal thing as I watched Mom shake water from an old, pale-green Coke bottle with a white sprinkler nozzle onto the still-to-be-ironed clothes. In amazement I watched her roll up the linen tablecloth and put it in the icebox. She repeated this with the napkins, as well.

"Why are you putting the ironing into the icebox?" I demanded.

"After you have gone off to school, I will iron them, but in the meantime the moisture and the cold helps. The damp and cold make the wrinkles iron flat. Now that's a lesson in housekeeping for you, my little one."

I wasn't even out the door yet and already I'd had two lessons.

My thoughts strayed to winter and the previous year in Huntsville, where the furnace burned wood, and the snow was so high we tobogganed off the roof of the woodshed. Here in Port Hope, there were still dried Hydrangea blossoms clinging to the tree beside the front walk. Although most gardens had been turned over and lay bare in brown strips along walkways, there was no sign of snow anywhere.

"When you get home, we will have a look at the new Eaton's catalogue and pick out a warm snowsuit and galoshes. You have outgrown your last year's ones," said Mom as she moved to the stove to stir the porridge. Mom made the worst oatmeal porridge in the world! Grandma tried and tried to teach her how to cook it slow and smooth, but no matter what, Mom always managed to make it hard and lumpy. We had to eat it anyway. "Sticks to your ribs," Dad always said. Anyway, he liked it hard, because his favourite lunch was sliced porridge fried in bacon grease. Of course he ate the bacon, too.

Breakfast changed. Sometimes instead of oatmeal porridge we had Cream of Wheat or Red River Cereal. Cream of Wheat was my first choice, especially with a spoonful of strawberry jam dropped on top. Oatmeal porridge was second choice, but I hated milk, so liked it runny with brown sugar; that is why I didn't like the way Mom cooked it. On Sunday, we had pancakes and maple syrup. Never did think much of that Red River stuff. It was in the same category as lentil soup. Dad loved lentil soup! We didn't eat that for breakfast, but every time there was a ham bone left from a roast, Dad took over the kitchen. "Irish," he said. "Only the Irish can make good lentil soup." Well, I liked to glue the lentils on paper to make pictures. I used to glue all sorts of stuff on paper: curly bits of string, dried grass, cotton batting, bits of silver foil; just about anything. I liked to drizzle paint over the glued-on stuff. Mom hung my pictures on the cellar door so everyone could see them. Ray did art, too, but he hid his pictures under his bed.

"Why doesn't Ray hang his pictures on the door?" I asked Mom.

"That's a tough one, kitten. You see, Ray wants to be the best and can't accept that his drawings are good enough to share. He is very talented, but shy about his ability. Perhaps someday he will begin to like his own work. The only reason his picture was in the fair was because his teacher insisted it be entered. That's really what he needs, more praise," she explained. "Probably from his father," I thought I heard her quietly mutter.

My talents were more in words and singing. Mom loved to sit at the piano in the dining room and leaf through old songbooks and play song after song. We did this most evenings. As soon as Mom opened the piano bench to pick out a selection of songbooks, Dad would hunker down in the old overstuffed chair beside the radio to read his paper. He never sang a note, but I think he enjoyed listening. Ray would find an excuse to run off to his room, but Mom and I would sing away to our hearts' content. She taught me just about every song in the books, and I would belt them out, thinking loud was best. I joined the school choir. The choir was learning Christmas songs for a concert, and our parents were going to come to the school and hear the choir and some kids reciting poetry.

Eaton's catalogue had just the right coat and leggings: a red plaid coat with navy pants. I picked white galoshes with white fur trim around the tops. Mom insisted on a hat with earflaps, "to keep your ears from getting frostbite." The snowsuit arrived with the hat and boots, but the snow didn't. The sun rose later in the mornings, and it got dark really early in the evening. We knew that as soon it got dark, we had to go in the house. The fireplace was lit most evenings to take the chill off, and the old furnace pumped up the heat. Even though there was no snow, I had to wear the snowsuit and boots anyway, just to keep warm. The rough wool leggings scratched and left my legs chapped, and I hated the hat.

The choir was practising a lot as it got closer to Christmas and the school concert. I stood right in the centre of the front row because I knew all the words to "Jingle Bells" and "Silent Night." The choir practised at recess and lunch so that we wouldn't miss any schoolwork. Our class was doing a skit about Christmas toys, and we got to practise that in class.

It seemed that Christmas was coming without snow. Everyone kept saying we might have a "green" Christmas. I did not really understand that until Mom explained that it meant we might not have snow in time for the holidays.

"Oh, no, that can't be! How will Santa get his sleigh here?"

"Well, kitten, Port Hope is a lot farther south then Huntsville and it doesn't snow as much here. But it will, you just wait. And you know what? Santa always finds a way."

"Well, it is no fun riding a bike in your snowsuit, and it is stupid not having snow."

I heard mother laughing as she walked away.

The very next morning, I wakened to large, fluffy snowflakes drifting by my window. When I raced to see, the trees were weighted to ground that was covered in white. Scarcely able to get my clothes on fast enough, I raced down the stairs and out the front door. Snow was everywhere.

"Mom! Did you see it?"

"Of course. Molly, bring in the milk, will you please?"

I reached out the front door for the bottle sitting on the top step to see the paper stopper lifted high above the bottle and frozen cream forced up beneath it. This became a science lesson as Mom explained that frozen liquids expand. I watched as the cream was removed carefully into a small bowl. When my glass of milk was poured, little crystals of ice floated in it.

"Don't drink it too fast, Mollikins, you will get a headache." But I *had* to drink it fast, I disliked it so.

I couldn't wait to gobble down my breakfast — even though it was Red River Cereal — and play in the snow. All the way to school, we flopped down on our backs whenever we saw a clear patch of white. We would move our arms up and down through the snow to create snow angels. A good-natured snowball fight erupted near the rink. Mostly we ducked in time, but some landed right on target. When we got into the schoolyard, Ralph Clayton hurled a whizzer that knocked the wind out of Ray when it connected with his back. Just then, a teacher put a stop to throwing snowballs but not making snow angels.

By the time the bell rang, my snow pants were sopping wet, as were my mitts. My galoshes were packed in snow and my shoes were wet. The floor of the coatroom, an alleyway behind the back wall of the classroom, had puddles of water under every hook. We all had to put on wet snowsuits when we went out for recess, lunch, and at the end of the day. We smelled of wet wool. Climbing into cold, damp suits was awful, but that didn't stop us from getting out to play in the snow. We rolled down the embankments, made snow angels, and slid on the frozen puddles all the way home.

I didn't want to go in the house. I played outside until it started to get dark. My sopping-wet snowsuit was hung behind the furnace to dry and my mitts were laid on a heat register with my galoshes. The house smelled like wet wool and hot rubber. Mom took one look at my hands and reached for the Vaseline. They were raw from the cold, but worse than that, the inside of my thighs burned and stung like crazy where the wet wool leggings had rubbed and chafed.

The next day was Saturday, and more snow had fallen during the night. Ray asked if he could take the toboggan across Ontario Street to Maybee's hill. I begged to go with him. Crossing Ontario Street was allowed only with strict instructions.

"You mind you look both ways — and watch the traffic. Hold Molly's hand and cross above Bloomsgrove," Mom ordered. "Be home in plenty of time before lunch. We have to go to the library this afternoon."

Mom was still giving instructions as we bailed out the front door and headed down Bloomsgrove Avenue. The traffic on Ontario Street was fierce, and we had to wait until all the trucks and cars passed. They were going both ways and, with the snow, they took forever to get past. Finally, we saw a clear stretch and pulled the toboggan full-speed across the road toward the excited babble coming from behind the third house on Martha Street. Sleighs, toboggans, dogs, and kids were scattered on the hill. We could hear laughter and shouting.

We quickly became a part of the activity, and the morning disappeared in a flurry of up-and-down hill scampering — or should I say, uphill scampering and downhill riding. Before we knew it, we were trudging home, sopping wet, with rosy cheeks and big smiles. The rosy cheeks were suspect the minute we got into the house, and the next thing I knew, zinc ointment was slathered on my face, my hands, and the insides of my legs. It didn't stop the chapping, and I suffered sore lips and chafed legs for the rest of the winter. Mom said it was my fair Irish skin, and I was going to have to live with it. As far as I could see, it was red and angry skin! When it wasn't red it was itchy, and Mom made me wear cotton gloves to bed so I wouldn't tear at the itchiness. I don't know why I had to suffer. Ray had no problem at all. Didn't he have Irish skin, too? It appears he may have inherited the Polish side of the family, and they were made of tougher stuff — or so he liked to lord over me.

Talk of the Christmas concert dominated the entire conversation at school. I was not only in the choir, but was to be a marionette in the classroom skit. It was all too exciting. The morning of the concert, I wakened to find that the red chapped skin was all over my body.

"Oh no!" Mom said. "I am sorry, honey, you will not be able to go to the concert, and we have to call the doctor. I think you have chicken pox." I didn't feel sick, just hot. I started to cry. My life was ruined!

"Mom, I *have* to go to the concert! I am the only one who knows all the words to 'Silent Night.' The whole thing will be ruined if I am not there!" I screamed.

Not only was I not allowed to go to the concert, I had to stay home from school for two weeks! The doctor put a quarantine sign on the door that announced to the world that I had chicken pox. And to make matters worse, I had to wear cotton gloves for three days so I wouldn't break the pox blisters and leave a scar. I started to feel really queasy and got a bit woozy, but the worst part was the itch. Mom made me wear the cotton gloves all day. She sat with me when I wasn't sleeping, laying cold cloths on my skin, reading to me, and playing "Fish." One day, Dad stayed home in the afternoon and let me help him develop pictures in his darkroom.

I spent most of my time cutting out pictures from the catalogue to glue into a scrapbook. Aunt Nell sent me a "get-well" present, a ballet colouring book and a whole box of new crayons. Ray went to the concert and, just to be nice, said I didn't miss anything. I knew I did. My colouring book did help to make up for missing the concert, and I did such a good job colouring the red Firebird that Mom mailed it to my aunt to show her how much I loved my book. I tucked in a thank-you note and said I would give her a big hug at Christmas, which was coming fast.

The chicken pox cleared up, and I was allowed to play with my friends in the snow again. The chapped lips and rash, which had left with the pox, returned to my ankles, wrists, and inner thighs, but being out in the snow made it all worthwhile. Ray and I made a humungous snowman in the backyard, wrapped a piece of red cloth around his neck for a scarf, and jammed in two lumps of coal for his eyes. Ray stuck a cork on the end of a stick to be a pretend corncob pipe.

❉ 13 ❉

CHRISTMAS

*O*ld Highway #2 was little changed. The 401 had bypassed the town and left the old highway meandering along the lake to Toronto, passing through small and large towns on its way.

School broke for the holidays, and Mother announced that we were going to Grandma's house for Christmas. Our house was always the gathering place for celebrations, so this was very big news.

Excitement mounted as Mom and Dad discussed the holiday plans. We were to go to Toronto the following Friday and on Saturday go downtown to see Eaton's Santa Claus parade. We would walk along the streets to see all the decorated windows then go to Eaton's store to see Santa Claus. I could give my Christmas wishes to Santa himself. Aunt Nell was even taking us to Dianna Sweets for lunch. The days couldn't fly away soon enough.

Mom had the old wringer washer working overtime. It sloshed around until the water had no bubbles, then the clothes were fed through the rollers perched above the tub. They emerged, squeezed flat, into the double concrete washtub on the left side. When all the clothes were out of the washer, Mom would then lift a lever and swing the rollers to hover between the two washtubs. Repositioning herself, she would scrape off some bluing into the rinse water, swish around the clothes, then feed them through the wringers into the right-hand tub, which had been filled with cold water.

"Cold water sets the bluing," she explained when I asked about her raw red hands reaching into the cold water. The cold clothes were then fed back through the wringer by Mom reaching behind — it wrung only one way — and catching the clothes as they came out the other side. She then tossed the thrice-squeezed laundry into a wicker basket. The three lines of clothesline strung across the cellar were chock full that Wednesday night. Thursday, Mom ironed the lot and sorted them into neat piles that were placed in a weathered leather suitcase, one pile for each person. After Dad left for work on Friday morning, his shaving kit was added, the buckles snapped shut, and the leather straps pulled tight and fastened. Ray and I went to school full of anticipation.

Dad came home from work early, and we loaded suitcase, food, presents, and a sick bucket for me into our old black '39 Ford. Arrangements had been made for Mr. Dixon to check on the house and animals. Flash went to stay with him at his house. The car was so loaded with stuff that Ray and I had to sit with our feet up on the suitcase. Off we set.

Our first stop was the Flying Dutchman at Bowmanville for a milkshake. I had butterscotch. Our next stop was near Whitby, where I left the milkshake at the side of the road. Whenever I got carsick, I usually fell asleep, and this was no exception. The next thing I knew, my Uncle Davey was lifting me off the car seat and setting me on the sidewalk at Grandma's house. Grandma was rushing down the steps to meet us, and Grandpa Richardson stood at the top step, puffing on his cigar. Grandpa Richardson was my grandma's second husband, since her first died a long time ago. My Uncle Bill and Uncle Davey were my mom's stepbrothers. "They came with the marriage," my dad explained.

Grandma was not much taller than me and spoke with a European accent. Grandpa Richardson was Scottish and really hard to understand. What a mix we were, with a Scottish brogue, an Irish lilt, and a European accent, mixed with those born in Canada. However, the animated greetings left no doubt that everyone was pleased to see us. We were hugged and shoulder slapped before being led into the house to smells of cabbage and roast beef. Luggage was disposed of, and we were herded into the dining room for dinner. I detested cabbage but picked at it anyway just to please my grandmother and not draw disapproving looks from Grandpa Richardson, who was referred to as Grandpa, but we had to call him Mr. Richardson. There was no talking at the table except to quietly request something be passed and we had to use our best manners. Eating was why we were at the table and that is what we did. At home, meals were an opportunity to out-shout each other in sharing the news of the day. Mr. Richardson did not approve of table conversation.

Right after supper, we gathered in the living room with the fireplace roaring. Mr. Richardson lit one of his disgusting cigars, and Dad had a cigarette. I excused myself to the kitchen to see Kelly, the new budgie, a blue one. Like Petie, he was the family pet and lived in his own cage in the kitchen and was allowed to fly free. He would sit on your shoulder and give you pecks on the cheek — bird kisses, Mom called them. I collected one of his blue feathers and took it upstairs to put in my scrapbook.

My grandfather lit the fire, and I started yelling at him that Kelly was loose and that it had been his fault for lighting the fire and letting Petie fly into it.

"I'll no' be hearing foul accusations agin me!" he shouted, pointing up the stairs.

Grandma was caging Kelly, and Mom was tugging me up the stairs, giving me a stern lecture on "accidents do happen" and that it was cruel to blame someone. She warned me not to speak with disrespect to one's elders, and when I was allowed to return I was to apologize to "Grandpa Richardson." I wasn't allowed back down until morning. Nervously I ventured into the living room ready to mutter, "I'm sorry, Mr. Richardson." The fire in the fireplace was out, there was no Grandpa Richardson, and there was no need to mention Petie or Kelly. Relief came when the only talk was about the parade. We were to go by streetcar!

"Are we really going on a streetcar?" I chirped as I skipped up Elmwood Avenue ahead of Mom, Aunt Nell, Uncle Dave, and Ray. Dad stayed at the house to read the newspaper, and Grandma stayed to cook supper. Riding on a streetcar was always a special adventure. We stood on the corner and watched for it, looking up the track that ran away into the distance. Before long, we saw the car turning the corner. It was red with cream stripes and had a sign that said "TTC" on the front. As Uncle Dave swung me up onto the step, he explained in answer to my question that it meant Toronto Transit Commission. Uncle Davey and I sat in a seat facing the front, and Mom and Aunt Nell sat right beside us on a bench facing sideways. Ray was hanging over the bar of the front seat stretching his neck to see what he could see. I crossed my fingers that I wouldn't get sick and I didn't. It was going to be a great day!

The crowds were fearsome, but we managed to find a good spot on Avenue Road right at the curb. By the time all the wonderful

ME WITH SANTA

floats with storybook characters and lots of paper flowers went by us, we had oohed and aahed until we were hoarse and waved until our arms were dead weight. We gathered up candies that were tossed in our direction and cheered Santa and his reindeer, riding high on a fire truck. My feet were numb with the cold. We had a few blocks to walk to the warmth of Dianna Sweets, and my toes were tingling hot by the time we smelled the most delicious hot chocolate in the whole world. We ordered scones with clotted cream and strawberries. By the time Mom was wiping the cream off my face with her ever-ready hanky wet with spit, we were ready for the next part of our adventure.

The windows at Eaton's College Street were alive with displays of mechanized scenes, just like the class diorama, only moving. One had a winter scene with a skating pond, and the skaters skated right across it, and toboggans went up and down the hill, and a horse-drawn sleigh went across the field. It was a miracle how they did that! The next window had Santa's Workshop, with all the elves as busy as could be. I stared and stared until I had to be dragged away.

Our next stop was to visit Santa himself. Imagine! I got to sit on his lap and whisper that I wanted skates for Christmas.

"Oh, ho ho," he laughed. "So you want to go ice skating, do you?"

"No," I replied. "Roller skates."

We left downtown Toronto and took the Bloor streetcar to Dundas Street then walked up the hill to Grandma's house. Hot soup was steaming in the pot, and freshly made sandwiches were pulled from the icebox and set by glasses filled with cold milk. I was too happy to complain about having to drink milk. Happily I went off to bed, knowing that Santa knew my one wish.

The next day, we visited my dad's family. We had cousins — three girls from one family and two girls and a boy from the other — but they were a lot older than me. Dad's two sisters spoke with Irish accents, as did their husbands. My cousins didn't. Ray explained that like us, they were raised in Canada and that was why. I didn't quite get it, but that was okay. We stayed late and had dinner (Aunt Charlotte let us talk at the table) before returning to Grandma's house.

The living room was a mess! The furniture had been moved, and a Christmas tree was now standing in the corner. Boxes and boxes of decorations were spread out everywhere. The living room drapes and blinds were drawn because of the blackout. Grandpa Richardson cleaned the fireplace so Santa could get down the chimney. The rest of us joined in to decorate the tree. Grandma had some very old decorations that she had set aside to be added last. Grandma's mother had brought them from Poland and they were extra special; when they were hung on the tree, it was almost religious. We each got to hang one! Mine was a large silver ball with lacy wire around it.

"Careful you don't break it; these balls are very special." I hung mine carefully and was proud to have been allowed to take part in such a privileged tradition.

"Mollikins," called Aunt Nell. "Look at the beautiful angel. It's up to you to put her on the very top."

Dad lifted me high, and I set the golden-haired angel right on the very top branch. Then everyone stood back, took a glass of wine from the tray Grandma passed around (even Ray and I were given small ones), Mom turned out the lights, and Uncle Dave plugged in the electric cord. We all cheered and clapped as the tree came to life. Every strand worked, and red, blue, green, and yellow lights glowed. There were special ones that looked like candles, and we watched them bubble up and down. It was sheer magic.

"A toast to all in good cheer," my grandfather's Scottish brogue called out. We touched each others' glasses and wished "Merry Christmas" all around.

"Children," stated Mother, "it is well past your bedtimes. Off you go."

I resisted, knowing I would never sleep, my head was so full of the past three days, and Christmas the very next morning. The next thing I knew, I smelled kielbasa being fried. I raced down the stairs and shrieked in delight when I saw the tree surrounded with presents. I headed right for them when my grandmother stopped me.

"Breakfast first, my girl. Come and set the table so we are ready when everyone else comes down."

"Hey, Grandma," I snickered, "I see you still leave your teeth in a glass. Why do you have to do that and why do you have false teeth, anyway?"

Grandma gave me one of those looks that said I shouldn't have spoken. She took the teeth out of the glass, rinsed them under the sink, and popped them into her mouth!

"I didn't look after my teeth when I was your age and they were so bad the dentist had to take out all my real ones and give me false teeth," explained Grandma. "That is why your mother is always after you to brush your teeth every day."

I thought it was really neat that she could take out her teeth. After many questions, I learned that she had to take them out when she went to bed, set them in a cleaning solution, and put them back in her mouth in the morning. That was almost as exciting as knowing Santa had come. Breakfast took forever, and I was sure we were never going to open the gifts, and on top of that we had to wait until Aunt Nell arrived. I was just busting!

Finally, the dishes washed and stored, we got to go to the living room, and Ray and I took down our stockings. They were full of candies with a big orange in the toe. Oranges were such a special treat; we seldom had them except at Christmas. Gifts were given one by one, in turn. I was very anxious for Mom to open the picture I coloured for her. I knew she was going to just love it — it was a red rose, and she was crazy about roses. I was very careful and hadn't gone out of the lines at all. I opened a white sweater cardigan from my grandparents, a blue dress with matching blue socks from my aunt, and a book of Main Street buildings from my uncle. All the buildings popped out and when they were carefully folded on the dotted lines, they stood up like real buildings. I looked beneath the tree to see if there was a box the right size for roller skates. There wasn't. I pouted as I watched others open gifts they seemed very happy to get. I was not happy I was not getting roller skates. Ray got a sweater, too, and other things. Finally, Mom handed me a very little box.

"And this is your very last gift. Open it, sweetheart."

I stared down at it, disappointed, but I was still curious to see what was in the box and managed a weak little smile, because one had to be thankful for what one got, didn't one?

I picked at the ribbon and toyed with the tape and uncovered a small jewellery box. I lifted off the lid and saw wads of cotton batting, I lifted away the top layer and sitting there was a key.

"A roller skate key!" I screamed. "Where are the skates?"

Everyone was laughing as Dad pulled them out from behind his back. "You should have seen your face, all screwed up at the little gift box. We sure played a good trick on you."

All the happiness and wine broke the "no talking at meals" rule, and there was so much talking going round that no one even noticed I didn't eat my turnips. Ray and I got a little sip of wine again to raise a toast to Grandma and the wonderful time we all shared. Then Mr. Richardson asked us to bow our heads and pray for Uncle Bill, who was far away at war, and for Uncle Davey, who was leaving to return to the war.

Uncle Davey helped me with skating on the sidewalk. It wasn't as easy as I thought it would be, especially in a snowsuit. The next afternoon, we waved goodbye as we set off to return to Port Hope.

❀ **14** ❀

USHERING IN 1945

I rounded the corner of Mill Street and pointed my old Buick up Walton. The fire station was no longer on Walton Street, nor was the police station. The ramshackle tenements had been renovated to be the in-place to live. I remember holding my nose to ward off the foul odour as I hurried past them to visit Dad at the police station or the fire station next door.

The days immediately following Christmas day were filled with fresh snow falling every day, beckoning Ray and me outside. Flash was ever close on my heels, her golden fur disappearing into snowdrifts. She followed all our activities, racing around us and running along wherever we went. She barked at the sleds' blades as they zoomed down the hill and licked our laughing faces when we arrived safely at the bottom. Chapped wrists from sodden woolen mittens and chapped inner thighs from soggy snowsuits did not deter us from buzzing like hornets all over the small sledding hill.

One nasty day with blowing wet snow, Patti had a fancy tea party. In the morning, she delivered real invitations made out of coloured paper to me, Beth, and Donna. We were to go to her house dressed in our Sunday best for three p.m. She was serving High Tea.

Mr. Miller opened the door and acted like a fancy butler and ushered three giggling girls to the dining room. The table had fancy dishes and a bouquet of real flowers in the centre. Warm sweet tea was served in a fancy china teapot, and we each had best-occasion cups like Mom used for her bridge players. Little decorated cookies were passed around by Patti, declaring, "Mom and I made them this morning." Patti's dad played the accordion and taught us how to do a country reel. Patti's dad told funny stories about catching lobsters, and that's how I learned he was from Nova Scotia, right beside a great big ocean, the Atlantic.

I had never seen a lobster, so he showed us pictures and pinched me a dandy just to show me how a lobster might grab me. I simply could not imagine eating anything so ugly. With their big pincers, they looked like goggle-eyed monsters from another planet. When the party was over, Patti's mom gave me a little packet of cookies for Ray, but I couldn't stop myself and I ate them all as I skipped home, being very careful not to splash the dirty wet slush on my best white stockings that Mom allowed me to wear for the High Tea. "Ladies must appear in their best for High Tea," she had said. Because Patti lived so close by, I was even allowed to go without leggings.

As I got near our house, I was starting to think how bad I was to have eaten Ray's cookies, when I saw Dad pull into the driveway. Quickly he got out of the car, ran around to the driver's side, yanked open the door, and helped Ray out. Ray looked very pale and seemed to be leaning into Dad.

"What's going on? Is Ray hurt?" I frantically asked.

Then I saw a sling and a cast on Ray's arm!

"Oh my gosh! Did you break your arm? How did it happen? Does it hurt awful? Did it hurt to get the cast on? How long before it comes off?" I rapid-fired as I held the door open for Ray and Dad. Nobody in our family had ever broken themselves before.

Ray was eased into the living room, where he was propped up on the sofa with pillows, Mom plumping and fussing. I felt doubly bad about the cookies now, so I brought Patches down to keep Ray company. Marmalade was lolling on the sofa back, pretending she was examining a large red flower in the fabric, but she was just waiting for Patches to begin a chase. Flash nuzzled sympathetically, knowing that something was wrong and Ray needed her sympathy. I pressed in beside Ray and demanded to know all. Ray seemed sleepy but told me his story anyway.

"Well, squirt, I did a very stupid thing. When I got home from Dougy's house nobody was here, so I thought I would be smart and climb in through my bedroom window. I climbed up on the back shed, like I always do, and as I was walking across the tin roof, I slipped on an icy patch and lost my footing. There was nothing to grab onto, so I just flew full tilt and hit the ground hard. I automatically reached out with my arm to stop the fall but my arm snapped and the pain was fearful. I guess I let out an awful roar because Mr.

Dixon heard me scream and came running. I never knew the old guy could move so fast!"

A weak smile spread across Ray's face. He winced and continued his account. "He stood me up and half carried me into his house. While Mrs. Dixon settled me in her rocking chair, Mr. Dixon called Dad, who rushed home and took me right to the hospital. Dad nonstop lectured me all the way there. The doctor, on the other hand, was really nice to me and kept asking if I felt woozy. My arm was so sore, I thought I might puke up my guts, but I didn't, and I didn't faint, either. The doctor told me how brave I was as he gave me a needle to kill the pain. The needle put my arm to sleep so I couldn't feel a thing, but watching the doctor twisting and pulling to set my arm in the right place made me feel real queasy.

"If I hadn't been so scared, I might have asked questions and learned about x-rays and getting a cast put on. The x-ray machine was this great big thing that they put me into and left me there while the technician wearing a big black apron that reached from her chin to her shoes held my arm. She kept telling me how brave I was, but I kept thinking how stupid I was and that I was definitely in trouble with Dad.

"The x-rays showed that I broke the tibia. The doctor said I was lucky it was a clean break. I asked what he meant and he told me that it wasn't shattered, just snapped. He said this means it will heal quicker.

"All the way home, Dad lectured me again about learning to be patient and waiting for Mom to get home next time. I guess I can't use my bedroom window any more to get in and out of the house. Ow!" Ray forgot for a minute and went to lift his broken arm.

Tears started to ease down Ray's cheeks, so I knew he was in pain. Mom came with a glass of water and some pain pills then gathered him in her arms and walked him to his bedroom "for a nap."

"Ray's really stupid," I announced as Mother came down the stairs.

"Molly, we all make mistakes. Ray's was a big one, and he will learn from it," she said with certainty. "It was an unfortunate accident. He is lucky it was only his arm that was injured — it could have been much worse. Ray is very uncomfortable and in pain and will be for some time. It will be several weeks before he gets the cast off, and I don't want you or anyone else teasing him or giving him a hard time. He has been through enough. Understand?"

I thought about this and little accidents I had had. My big brother was hurt and I ate all his cookies. I never did tell him that! But I do think it made me feel more sympathy for his misadventure.

Ray's accident changed our holiday activities, because now he couldn't go sledding, and I couldn't go by myself. I discovered I could beat Ray at "Snap," because he only had one arm and couldn't get the cards down fast enough. So I wanted to play Snap all the time. We did play Monopoly and read comics, too, to help the time pass.

Mom planned a special New Year's dinner. We had red, green, and blue shiny paper party hats and colourful horns that unrolled into a long paper strip when you blew them. We had other shaking noisemakers as well. Mom sent Ray and me to bed early in the evening with the promise that she would wake us just before midnight to see the New Year in. What an adventure that was going to be; I had never been up at midnight before! I helped decorate the table and set the hats and horns next to every plate. I was really, really tempted to blow the horns, even though I was warned that it would bring bad luck if they were blown before midnight. Mom got out the fancy silver candlesticks and some green candles that smelled kind of strange.

"They are bayberry candles," explained Mom. "I grew up in a Polish community, and they were always a part of the special holiday tradition."

"Where did you grow up?" I asked, not realizing before that she had not always been just right where we were and that she had once been a child.

"Manitoba. Until I was ten." The conversation ended abruptly.

When I went to bed, Mom set out my best sweater and plaid skirt to wear for our midnight dinner. Even though it was in our house and only our family, we still had to dress for the occasion. Smells of cloves and ham filled the house, because we were going to have a special celebration meal after midnight to welcome in 1945. I knew Dad's lentil soup would be on next week's menu.

Before I knew it, Ray called into my room, "Time to get up, squirt!" When I came downstairs, the whole house smelled of cloves, ham, and bayberry. The blinds were all drawn, the Christmas tree in the living room shone brightly, and the embers in the fireplace glowed. In the dining room, the soft light of candles made everything look like a fairyland. The radio was blaring and full of static.

"Why is the radio on so loud?" I asked.

"They are broadcasting from Times Square in New York. Usually they are outside with a huge celebration, but because of the war, this year the broadcast is from inside the studios. When they count down to 'one,' then it will be 1945," Ray explained with authority, his arm with the cast resting on the top of the radio as he leaned in to hear every word. I danced around with a fancy paper hat on my head controlling myself not to blow the silver horn I clutched in my hand.

"Quiet, everyone," yelled Dad with his ear to the speaker. "Five, four, three, two, one — HAPPY NEW YEAR!"

Mom kissed me, Dad kissed me, and Ray even kissed me! Everyone blew horns and laughed. The radio was playing loud music, and we could hear yelling in the background. Then Dad kissed Mom for a long time! Ray looked at me and winked.

"Everyone has to make a New Year's resolution," announced Mom. Seeing my puzzled expression, she explained, "At the start of each year, we make a promise to keep for the next year. It can be a secret, but you have to be true to yourself and keep the resolution." I resolved not to eat any cookies that Mrs. Miller might give me for Ray in 1945.

Dinner was a festive affair. Ray and I blew our horns every chance we got and pinched each other in fun. We had ham, peas, squash, and potatoes mashed with a little butter — not margarine, *real* butter. We even had Parker House dinner rolls, and each of us had a pat of butter on a side plate for our roll. Mom must have saved and saved ration stamps to get butter!

"Pass the rolls!" Ray demanded.

"Please!" corrected Mom.

The rolls didn't come fast enough for Ray so he stood up to reach over a candle to grab the plate. Mom started to scold when I saw Dad lurch for Ray. Flames flared up Ray's doeskin shirt sleeve, and when he reached to wipe them away with the broken arm, the cast arm went on fire, too! I started to scream and ran in terror to the living room and sought safety under the sofa cushions, screaming and screaming that Ray was going to die. I just knew he was going up in flames and would burn to death. The next thing I knew, a strong hand grasped my arm and dragged me out from under the cushions and pulled me to my feet.

"Young lady, get control of yourself! The worst thing you can do in an emergency is panic," my father was tersely saying as he firmly held me by the shoulders. I was sure he was going to give me a good shaking, but he didn't. "Ray is fine, the fire is out. He is upstairs changing his shirt. But you, Molly, must learn not to overreact in that scatterbrained way of yours; never, never cause such a commotion again in a critical situation. I needed to help Ray, and you were nothing but disruptive."

He stormed away, leaving me standing there feeling as if *I* were to blame that Ray caught fire. It wasn't fair. Mom came over and put her arm around me and assured me that if I dried my tears, there would be apple pie and ice cream for dessert. The ever-ready hankie appeared, and I gave a good blow and ceased sniffling. We finished our meal, toasted the New Year, and wished everyone happiness. I glared at Ray, who glared back. We both knew that I had been scared to death because I didn't want him hurt again, but I couldn't ever say that to his face.

Mom pondered, "Things happen in threes. What will happen to Ray next?"

It didn't take long to find out. Three days after we were back at school, Ray was horsing around with his buddies in the playground and got an elbow in the eye. He blamed Ralph Skinner, but nobody knew for sure; it was just one of those accidents. Now Ray had a cast on his arm with hundreds of names scribbled on it and a black eye. He looked fearsome. He was the envy of all the boys in school, and the girls giggled when he walked past.

The big day finally came for the return visit to the doctor to get Ray's cast off. He brought the dirty thing home as a souvenir. He left it sitting on his dresser until it got dusty, then it just disappeared. Nineteen forty-five had all the promise of being an interesting year; it had started out with lots of excitement.

✾ 15 ✾

JANUARY 1945

Lucy came back to school after being away for four whole months. Miss Weldon brought her into the classroom in a wheelchair! She had a brown woolly blanket draped over her knees that we learned hid ugly braces on her legs. Her beautiful blonde curls were dark and dull, and she was very pale, but a smile sent my way lit up my heart. I was so excited to see her that I hugged her and hugged her. Lucy was far from well and only strong enough to come to school half days, in the morning. When I saw how sick she looked, I understood why my mother and father had made such a fuss over me and I thanked my lucky stars that I had not caught that awful polio.

I became Lucy's constant companion and waited on her every wish. The big black braces on her legs didn't hide all her pale, almost see-through skin. Her eyes were not bright and lively like they used to be. Everything she did required a lot of effort, and she would get very tired before the morning was over. When that happened, Miss Weldon called Lucy's dad, and he came with their car and took her home. Lucy wasn't allowed to go outside to the playground for fear she might catch a chill or a cold, even though she said she was taking medicine just to keep her from getting a nasty germ. This was probably a good thing, because she would have been terribly unhappy to have to go back into the hospital. She told me how she really hated being there.

I tried to keep her happy while she was inside and not able to run around outside and doing acrobatics on the roll bar; she loved doing that and, before she got sick, she could flip around faster than anyone else. I was allowed to stay inside the classroom with her, and we did puzzles, coloured, and read books. I pushed her wheelchair around, sharpened her pencils until they were as pointy as could be, and got her exercise book from Miss Weldon when it had gone in for marking.

Lucy wasn't strong enough to come to school every day, but as the weeks passed, she managed more and more full mornings without having to call her dad. We became such fast friends, sharing all our secrets; and Lucy told me all about having the polio and how scared her family was that she might die! We whispered silly things like how when we laughed with food in our mouth it blew out our nose, which always set us to giggling very quickly. Like the day Kenny gave his speech.

Public speaking competitions were right up there with playing the piano and singing: a chance to show off. If you were the best in the school, you got to go to Peterborough to the Kiwanis Festival and if you were the best *there*, you got a certificate to bring home. I didn't know how to play the piano, but I had no problem opening my mouth to give a speech or sing a song. Everyone had to do a speech in class as a part of our lessons. Some kids were just awful, you couldn't hear them or they talked about really boring things like Emperors in China or how their mother made fruit cake for Christmas. We had to sit with our hands on our desks and listen anyway and pretend we really liked what was being said. We had to clap even if they were really bad. Miss Weldon gave us marks for "effort," even when it was not great.

Well, Kenny's speech wasn't really bad, and he spoke up so everyone could hear. It was what he talked about that got the class to giggling. He chose to talk about worms, and specifically tapeworms! This involved a lesson on specific parts of our innards as necessary information. Yuck! Anyway, in the recess period, Lucy and I just couldn't stop laughing. We were pretty used to being dosed regularly for roundworms, so the very thought of passing long, skinny, tapeworms was hilarious. "Do you think Kenny got his information at the library?" I asked holding in my sides, doubled over with giggles, "or from personal experience?"

I gave a speech on what you might see in all four seasons if you went walking in the woods. I was picked as the best in my class and had to say my speech at a special evening at the school. Our parents came and there were judges and everything. Before that big night, Dad gave me lots of coaching on how to pause, look the audience in the eye, and speak clearly to the back of the room. Dad spoke at lots of grown-up events, so he really knew how to do it. I won third place!

It was the first time a Grade 2 kid had ever won, and everyone made a big fuss over me.

You might think I would be very happy about this, but I was terrified. The three winners had to represent the school at the Kiwanis Festival, and I knew I would die of embarrassment, for I was sure to get carsick on the drive to Peterborough. Dad decided that the whole family should go, and we would go in our car. Getting sick with your own family is a whole lot better than with strangers, so off I went.

The festival was a very big event for the schools, and kids came from all over the place. When we got there, Mom went to a table just inside the big doors of the church hall where the festival was held and where two people sat to check in the contestants. A lady wearing a dark green dress with a white collar and a hat on her head with feathers bunched over her left ear gave Mom a piece of paper that told us when I was to speak.

"Oh, sweetheart, this is good news! You will only compete with students in Grades 2 and 3. I was concerned they would include older classes and you would be competing against kids that were much more experienced than you."

We sat in the hall on hard folding chairs for what seemed hours as some grown-ups talked and talked about the festival and the judges and how long it had been going on. I was just starting to doze off when they announced the start of the speeches. I sat up and was getting very nervous as I listened to my competitors, because they were all as good as me, or better. I knew I had to remember every word and not make a mistake, because I wanted to take home a certificate with my name on it. My biggest fear was pronouncing "adjudicators." I picked at my new white socks and twisted the hem of my skirt. By the fourth speaker, I was chewing the ruff on the shoulders of my starched pinafore. A swift move by my mother stopped that; then I heard my name called.

"Ladies and gentlemen; fellow students; adjudicators, my speech today is called 'A Walk in the Woods.'" I relaxed as soon as "adjudicators" was out and I smiled at the judges as I said the rest. Everyone clapped when I bowed at the end, but I knew they clapped anyway. Mom squeezed my hand when I returned to my seat and said, "Well done!" and Dad nodded in agreement. I smiled, pleased as punch that they were happy.

Mom was dressed in her best daytime suit, navy blue with white piping and buttons. The skirt had pleats that she kept as "sharp as a knife" by folding it one pleat at a time and placing it carefully under her mattress. She had matching shoes and a purse with a gold clasp that she kept nervously opening and closing. Then she sat very still with her hands grasping the purse tightly. The veil on her hat was pushed back so she would not miss seeing every little thing. She listened carefully to each word of all the speeches and now leaned forward to hear the judges. After everyone finished speaking, the head judge gave a report, not to say bad things about our speaking, but to help us improve for the next time. This was called the adjudication, Mom explained.

They told me I had chosen a good topic and spoke very well! I smiled all the way to the platform to collect my certificate for First Place. As a special treat, Dad took us to a fancy restaurant for dinner, and I got to have a Shirley Temple as a reward. The next morning, Saturday, while Ray and I went to the library, Dad framed my certificate and hung it on my bedroom wall over my desk where I could see it the instant I opened my eyes every morning.

Books were my favourite things, and the library one of my favourite places. Every Saturday morning, I would buddy ride behind Ray on his bike and we would cruise down Ontario Street to Walton, weave along the path beside the railway tracks, cut through the alley beside the theatre, and cross to the public library on Queen Street.

We belonged to the stamp club. It met first thing in the morning in a room in the basement of the library. We talked about lots of places and looked at different stamps. The leader, Stan Young, would allow us to buy individual stamps or a packet of mixed stamps from other countries. I always bought a mix and was careful to put them in my special stamp book with little "hinges" that wouldn't hurt the stamp. The stamp books had places to put stamps from every country and had black and white pictures of many of the stamps. When the colourful stamps were added, the pages came alive with colour. I wanted to fill every space. Sometimes when we had doubles we got to trade them for ones we didn't have. That way everyone had a better chance of filling their book.

After the meeting, when I had carefully pocketed my new packet of stamps, I searched through the Children's Library looking for new reading books to take home. I always gathered up as many as Ray's bicycle carrier would hold. Ray took only one, just to make Mom happy. He preferred reading *Flash Gordon* or *Dick Tracy* comics. He had a whole stack of them on the floor of his bedroom beside his bed. Trading comics was something we all did; that way, we got to read a whole mess of them when we only had allowance money for one. Mom didn't get mad at Ray for reading comics. She just said, "Reading anything is good reading." (Mom should know, she wrote articles for the newspaper.)

The children's section of the library was separate from the adult section. It was in the basement. Sometimes I went with Mom to the grown-up part. Ray went to art class there because he was so good at drawing. This was how our Saturdays went, library in the morning, home for lunch, and a movie matinee in the afternoon.

Lucy wasn't allowed to go to the matinee or the library or anything. I hated the Infantile Paralysis. Mom said the best news was that no other children had contracted the disease. I sure wish Lucy hadn't. Now that she was back at school and no longer "contagious," I could go to her house. I would take a library book with me, and we would read it together.

One day, Ray and I arrived home from school to find Mom slouched over the kitchen table wringing a wet handkerchief as she sobbed and sobbed. This scared us because we had never seen Mom or Dad cry.

"Oh, my darlings, our playful Uncle Dave has been shot down over Germany. He is missing in action. I'm so frightened for him."

I knew both my uncles were pilots in the Royal Air Force, but I never thought Hitler would have them shot down! I got very angry at that Hitler. I never knew Leo's father, but my Uncle Dave was mine and he was my special buddy and I didn't want him to be shot down dead. It was a difficult time for the whole family. The worst part about it was that Uncle Dave was just gone! Shot down out of the sky somewhere over Germany. None of us knew if we would ever see him again.

Grandpa Richardson, Grandma, and Aunt Nell came to stay with us so the family could be together. There was a hush about the house, eyes were dabbed with hankies, voices spoke in whispers, and lots of hugging was going on. Then one day Mom answered the phone

UNCLE DAVEY

to learn that the dreaded telegram had arrived: "We are sorry to inform you that David Ballantyne Richardson was killed in action."

At school we had a list up on the wall of the hallway where students from all the classes wrote names of family members who had been killed in the war. When someone was killed, the teacher made an announcement, showed us where on the map it happened, and told us to be especially proud of the men and women in service. Nearly everyone in my class had a name, some more than one, on that list. I added Uncle Dave.

Lucy helped me to be sad; she understood. She told me I should make a scrapbook with all the things I remembered about my Uncle Dave so I would never, never forget him. All I could remember was his beautiful smile and that couldn't be put in a scrapbook; but I knew I would never forget it, ever.

❀ 16 ❀

SECRET LOVE

One snowy February day when I was getting dressed for recess, I bent over to put on my white rubber galoshes. Slipping my foot carefully past the wet fur trim to avoid getting that clammy wet fur on the bare spot above my ankle socks and holding the strap so it wouldn't get caught inside the boot, I felt something weird. I stepped out of the boot and reached in to pull out a crumpled piece of glossy paper. As soon as I unfolded it, I saw that it was a valentine. It had a bright red heart with "I love ya" on it, but nobody had signed it. I looked at everyone in the classroom, but nobody was looking my way.

"Hey, which one of you put this card in my boot?" I yelled. Nobody answered.

The next day, I found another valentine in my boot, exactly the same as the one I found the previous day. It, too, was not signed. Now I was *really* curious and just *had* to know whom they were coming from, but when I asked out loud, nobody owned up. Another card showed up the following day. They all had the same red hearts with "I love ya" on them and no name. All the kids in the class were now taking notice and starting to tease that I had a secret boyfriend. I know I got as red as a beet and held my hands over my ears whenever they started teasing, "*Molly's got a boyfriend!*"

With Valentine's Day fast approaching, Miss Weldon put a big box at the front of the room with a slot in the top and explained. "Class, this is our class mailbox. You can put your valentine cards in here, and on Valentine's Day we will distribute them all. Every class has a box, so if you have a card for another class, you have permission to go into the classroom at lunchtime or recess and drop your cards in their box. It is a nice way of saying you are a friend."

Yeah, well, I had one and didn't even know who it was!

With our weekly allowance money, Donna, Patti, and I bought big books of valentine cards and cut them out when we got home.

Later, I started to carefully fill out my friends' names. "Mom, how do you spell 'Elaine'?" I hollered. Mom came and sat by me and helped me spell names. I did my best printing.

"Is that everyone in your class?" she asked.

"No, I'm not sending one to stupid Allan Smith, he is a stinky boy. And Mary Granger is retarded."

"Now, Molly, that is not nice. Perhaps Allan does not have anyone at home who takes good care of him. And poor Mary can't help that she was born the way she is. Both of them deserve a card far more than your other friends."

"No way! I am not going to give them a card. I will be laughed all the way from Port Hope to Huntsville. The rest of the kids will never let me forget it."

"Okay, let's think how you would feel if you were Allan or Mary. Can you imagine how you would feel if everyone in the class got cards and you did not? That would be very disappointing, wouldn't it? You would be very hurt and think no one liked you."

I thought about this and knew that Allan and Mary would never get cards from any of the other kids in the class, but I didn't want to give them one, either. "Can I give them one without my name on it?" I asked in a sullen voice, knowing I would be in trouble if I didn't agree.

"That is better than not giving them one at all — but why don't you sign it 'a friend.' That way they might feel that someone cares a little bit."

The next day when Miss Weldon handed out the cards, I watched Allan and Mary, terrified that someone would know who "a friend" was. Each got a card from Miss Weldon and only one other card. I watched them as they hugged the card close then looked about the room to see if they could see "a friend." I sank deep in my chair pretending to be studying my cards.

"Miss Weldon, I got a card from you and another one, too!" yelled Mary, waving the cards high with delight.

"Why, Mary, how wonderful! Let me see," said Miss Weldon as she took a good look at the cards.

As the class was leaving for the day, Miss Weldon came up behind me and whispered in my ear, "Molly, that was a very nice thing you did for Mary and Allan. It doesn't matter that your name wasn't on them but never be afraid to own up to good deeds."

FLASH

I never did figure out how she knew it was me, but teachers were smart and knew things. I don't know why, but I had nice fuzzy feelings after that and hopscotched all the way home. I got twenty-two cards but none of them made me feel as good as the one I got with "Mary" written on it in great, squiggly letters that trailed down to the bottom edge of the card.

When I got home, Flash met me at the door with her tail wagging and love pouring out her eyes. I gave her a big hug for Valentine's Day, knowing she loved me back. Somehow I hoped Mary and Allan had a dog.

The next day was Saturday, and while Mom was brushing my hair, she leaned over and picked up first one of my hands then the other. "Mollikins, your fingernails are filthy! However did you let them get so dirty?"

"I dunno. They just get that way."

With that, Mom rolled up my sweater sleeves and inspected my elbows. "What do you do in the bath?" She exclaimed in horror.

"Your elbows are black and your upper arms are streaked with dirt. Get on up to the tub and we will sort this out right now!"

I was getting to be a big girl now, and Mom didn't have to bathe me anymore. I had to admit that I spent most of the time in the tub blowing bubbles with my bubble pipe, trying to blow them higher and higher before they popped. Then when the bubble soap was all gone, I would just get out and dry off. I looked at my elbows and arms, and sure enough, they were dirty, all right. Mom arrived in the bathroom armed with a nailbrush and face cloth. She went viciously at my elbows with that hard brush! I was sure there wouldn't be any skin left when she was finished.

"Ow, stop it!" I yelled, twisting to get out of her firm grasp without any luck at all. The next thing I knew, the cloth was rubbing my arms raw, and she didn't stop there. My face was scrubbed red and my feet were given the nailbrush treatment as well. Once I was towelled dry, out came the nail clippers and file. Mom dug every bit of grit out and gave me a stern warning that if I didn't meet inspection every day, she would have a go at me again. That nasty lesson taught me to wash first, then play bubbles.

On Monday at school, I snuck a glance at Allan's fingernails, only to see that his hands were totally filthy. The back of his neck was grimy, too. I just bet Mom was right: no one at his house cared enough to scrub the dickens out of him. Somehow the scrubbing Mom gave me now felt warm and special. Mary wasn't at school that day.

The principal ducked his head in through the door of the classroom and signalled Miss Weldon to go out to the hallway. She placed the chalk she was writing with on the ledge of the blackboard and, leaving the door open, went to speak with the principal. We could hear whisperings, then "Oh, no!" from Miss Weldon as the door was slammed shut and she disappeared into the hallway. My classmates and I looked at the door and at each other with puzzled looks on our faces. After a while, the door opened and Miss Weldon returned to the classroom. Her eyes were red and she looked very upset. However, there was no explanation, even though we were just busting to know what had gone on.

When I got home after school, Mom was on the phone, so I just headed for the kitchen, threw my boots behind the stove, and hung my snowsuit on my hook. I plopped in a chair and grabbed the snack that Mom always had set out on the table for Ray and me. Mom startled me as she came silently up behind and put her arms around my shoulders and hugged me tight. My Mom was a hugger, that is for sure, but this hug was different, almost like when Lucy got sick.

"What's wrong?"

"Oh, honey, sometimes terrible things happen. Your Dad called to tell me that he had just dealt with a very disturbing case. Some people just don't deserve to have children."

Mom moved away and put on the kettle to brew a pot of tea and busied herself getting a cup, saucer, and milk, while I waited to hear what else she had to say. She returned to the table, gathered her cotton housedress around her, and sat heavily in a chair across from me. She stirred the milk into her tea, staring at a spot on the table where nothing was there to see.

"Well, what happened?" I was impatient to know.

"What? Oh, that. You needn't bother pretty your little head about it. It was just police business."

I hadn't a clue as to what she was talking about. Grabbing an apple out of the bowl and some comic books off the shelf, I sprawled out on the living room rug.

"Molly," Mom said as she walked into the room wringing her hands dry on her apron. "What is the name of the little girl in your class, Mary what?"

"You mean Retard?'

"Molly, stop it! That is not nice, and I won't have you speaking ill of people who cannot help themselves."

"Sorry," I murmured. "Granger."

"Oh, dear!" Mom exclaimed.

"Why?" I queried, now lying on my back looking up at Mom standing in the doorway. She had a look on her face that told me she was deep in thought.

"Uh, nothing. Don't you worry," I heard Mom say as she turned and went up the stairs.

"Well, I'll be! Now that's *three* things I don't have an answer for!"

When Dad came home, he and Mom had a little whispering session in the kitchen, then Dad strode into the living room.

"Molly, come here for a minute. I have something to tell you."

Leaving my comics strewn across the floor and the apple core on the carpet, I perched on the arm of the sofa beside Dad.

"You know Mary Granger? I believe she is in your class. Well, she has had a very nasty accident. Her father left a loaded gun in the closet without the safety latch on, and when Mary reached for her coat to go to school, she tipped it over. The gun landed against the door jamb and discharged."

"Holy cow! Did she get hurt?"

"It was a terrible accident, Molly. Mary was killed instantly."

"Killed! You mean she's dead?"

"Yes."

I felt really awful. Even though she was not someone I really liked, she was in my class and didn't deserve to be dead just because someone had left their stupid gun in the closet with ammunition in it and everything.

"Now perhaps you understand why I am always extra careful with my guns and why I forbid you and Ray to touch them. I have to have my revolver for work and my rifles and shotgun for hunting, but I would never, never leave them loaded. In fact, I always keep the ammunition well out of reach. Promise me you will never touch the guns, regardless."

I had no interest in silly old guns anyway, so I nodded.

The next day at school, Miss Weldon choked out the story about Mary even though we had all been talking about it already. I looked over at Mary's empty desk. It was almost as if her shadow were still there, and I felt real sad and kind of lonely.

"Class, we are going to write a letter to Mary's parents. It is called a letter of condolence, and in it we will tell them how sad we are to have learned of Mary's unfortunate accident. There will be a church service on Thursday, and I have arranged for the class to attend. We will walk over to the church and sit together then return to school in time for recess. It is very sad to lose someone you know, and I want you all to be on your best behaviour at the church."

As I sat in the church, I stared at the back of Mary's father's head and thought bad thoughts about him for being so careless. Then the minister mentioned that her friends were in the congregation. Ryan Stacey leaned into me and whispered with his stinky breath in my ear, "Retard had no friends." I gave him a dirty look and thought how glad I was that I had sent Mary a card for Valentine's signed "a friend" and that I had taped her card up on my mirror.

❋ **17** ❋

BAKING AND ICE

I wandered up Ontario Street. Smells of fresh-baked bread filled the air, and I was delighted to see that a bakery still existed where Broadbent's Bakery used to be. Mr. Broadbent would give out big sugar cookies whenever Ray and I accompanied Mom to pick up two loaves of golden-crusted bread.

"Don't slam the door!" Mom yelled from the kitchen. She greeted us nearly every day with this demand, but always too late. "Don't leave your boots and coats heaped on the floor." I never quite understood how she knew, but according to Mom, she could see through walls, and we could hide nothing from her ever-searching eyes.

Bending to retrieve my damp coat and boots, I grudgingly gathered them to my chest and with heavy steps took them down the cellar stairs to hang them on my designated hook. My irritation forgotten as quickly as it appeared, I raced upstairs, grabbed a thick-cut slice of Broadbent's delicious bread and, slathering it with honey, I settled in to tell about my day.

"Miss Weldon says we are going to write a cookbook, and when it is finished, we all get one to keep. All of us have to bring in a favourite recipe to put in the book so we will have twenty recipes, maybe twenty-one, if Miss Weldon brings one, too. We have to bring in a sample of the food, too. I want to take the super duper chocolate fudge recipe. Can I? Or maybe the ginger cookies recipe?"

"Did Mrs. Elliott say anything about your being able to cook this by yourself?" asked Mom.

"Well, yah, but nobody is going to do that. We will just get our moms to do the cooking."

"And what would that teach you?"

"Nothing. I don't think it is about teaching anything — just something to do."

"I don't think so. Baking and cooking are great ways to teach mathematics, reading comprehension, co-operation, and science. I expect this is what Miss Weldon is trying to achieve here," stated Mom as she read the note I brought home from school about the cookbook project.

"Mmmm, suppose so," I mumbled with a mouth full of bread and honey.

"Ginger cookies it is. I do not have enough brown sugar to do fudge. Tomorrow is Saturday, and before you head off to the library, we will bake a batch of cookies for the class and write out the recipe as Miss Weldon has instructed."

Saturday morning was grey and damp — "a *dreak* day," as my dad would say. I asked him once what *dreak* meant, and he said it was an old Irish word that combined "drab" and "bleak" into one word. On this kind of dreak day, baking was the perfect start to the day. I swallowed my Cream of Wheat (Mom made it really runny so it was just right for brown sugar and no milk) and slathered a piece of bread with grape jelly, avoiding the Oleomargarine, and chomped off big bites between gulps of steaming Ovaltine.

"I thought we were making cookies," I mumbled as I tried to stretch my tongue long enough to lick jam off my chin. "Why isn't the cookie dough ready?"

"Now that, my dear, is what *you* are going to do — not me."

"Me! But you always do the baking! I don't know how."

"Well Mollikins, after today you *will* know how. Now put your dishes in the sink and we will get started."

I gathered up my plate, cup, and knife and, standing on tiptoes, set them in the deep well of the sink. That chore finished, I plunked myself back down on the chair.

"Up you get! First you have to organize yourself. Here, read the recipe and gather all the ingredients and put them on the table. You will also need a large mixing bowl, a spatula, a measuring cup, measuring spoons, waxed paper, cookie sheets, and a knife." Mom gave these directions as she scrubbed off the surface of the table and spread a clean linen towel over the cleaned area. She pointed at the list of ingredients, tied an apron around my waist and one around hers, too, and set to watching me reaching for all the stuff out of the kitchen cupboards.

Eagerly, I gathered together the milk, flour, sugar, lard, and ginger (Mom had to spell out the word "ginger" for me) and placed them beside the mixing bowl. I placed the rest of the stuff on the table, too, then watched Mom tidy them into a concentrated spot instead of being spread all over the place. I knew from the exaggerated way she did this that she was not impressed with where I had put them and wanted me to take notice. She muttered, "Being well organized means being neat." Now that I had brought Mom all the stuff she needed, I hopped up on the chair to watch.

"Young lady, the point of this exercise is that *you* are making the cookies."

"I am? Okay! What do I do next?"

"Look at your recipe — now read how much flour is needed."

"Two cups."

"Okay, now look at the measuring cup and see where it says two cups."

It was the first time I knew that a measuring cup said anything. I looked at the side and there were a lot of funny-looking numbers, and right at the top it said, "2 cups." "What are these funny numbers? There is a one on top of a two."

"Those are fractions, meaning *part* of a number. Here, let me show you." Mom explained how the fractions worked and that they were very important to know about when you were cooking or you could make awful-tasting stuff. She also explained that it was important to pay attention to those numbers or the baking might not work. They were all measured for the best results, and mixing in the right proportions was science. She showed me that the spoons were special sizes, too.

Very carefully, I measured the flour, sugar, lard, and ginger into the bowl, then added the milk bit by bit, mixing it with the spatula. My arm started to get tired as the batter thickened. Mom did give it a little extra mix just to "add a little mother's love," she said. Next, she had me put a long piece of waxed paper on the table, onto which I dumped the dough. Now this part I had done before, so I knew that I had to spread the dough along the wax paper and then roll it into a firm tube. Mom instructed me to get it the same diameter from end to end. "More mathematics," she said; "geometry." Whatever that was . . . anyway, she seemed to think she was teaching me something.

"Now take the bread knife and very carefully slice very thin wafers evenly from the roll and place them on the cookie sheet; but before you do, make sure the oven is at 350 degrees." Seeing my puzzled look, she explained that the numbers 3, 5, 0 made 350. I peered at the dial on the front of the oven door and nodded that it was just right. Mom added another shovelful of coal to "hold the temperature" then showed me how cut the cookies.

"Hold the knife by the handle and place the heel of your hand on the back of the tip of the blade, set it on the rolled dough, and push." Before long, the cookie sheets were covered in lots of little rounds of dough ready for the oven. My apron was covered in flour, as were my arms and chin. "You are wearing a baker's badge of honour," Mom laughed as she wiped a smudge off my nose with a tea towel. I was tickled pink that I had made the cookies all by myself and couldn't wait to be the taste tester.

"Now, go wash up, because we have to write out the recipe while the cookies are baking." Off I skipped to return clean as a whistle, ready for the task of writing the recipe. I carefully scripted each letter and number, not easy for me with my left-handedness, but Mom said I did a great job. The smell of ginger filled the house. While I was washing up, Mom made another batch just so we would have some for ourselves.

A thought came to me. "Mom," I said, "I never did find out who left those valentines in my boot. Sure is weird."

Mom started to laugh and got that funny little I-know-something-you-don't look on her face.

"I think someone was playing a trick on you and you might never find out who — but it is kind of fun to have a secret admirer, isn't it?" I wasn't so sure, but nodded anyway.

Munching on a warm cookie, I hollered for Ray to "Come and get one while they are warm!" before we headed out to the library. We had to hurry, as the morning had just flown by. There was no reply, so I went to fetch him in his bedroom. When I pushed open his door, I caught him quickly stuffing a box of valentine hearts with "I love ya" on them into his desk drawer. I pretended not to see, but grinned to myself, pleased that the mystery was solved and a little pleased that my brother loved me, even though he didn't want me to know.

"Molly, Ray, I want you to come right home from the library today, as your father wants to take some pictures of the two of you with his new Graphlex."

"Aw, Mom," whined Ray, "Dougy and I were going to walk down to the beach to see the ice floes. We heard they are breaking away from shore and are awesome."

"Yes. And dangerous, too! You are absolutely not going to the beach!"

Ray grumbled all the way to the library about how he wasn't allowed to do anything and that he was treated like a baby.

When we got home, Dad had his tripod set up and his head level with the bellows at the back of his new camera. I never could figure out how he took such good pictures when everything in the viewfinder was upside-down. On the chesterfield were a couple of cowboy hats from our costume cupboard. The piano bench sat in the middle of the room with a blanket over it. Sitting us on the piano bench, Dad snapped away, muttering, adjusting spotlights, moving us this way and that before he would say, "Hold still, now. Look at my hand." Then he would press the shutter plunger, looking very satisfied.

"Stupid way to spend a Saturday," grumbled Ray. "I wanted to go see the ice jams."

"Good idea! Grab your coats and cameras. We can make an adventure out of it." Mom was smiling from the doorway, her arms loaded with coats and hats. She pulled my hat tight over my ears and patted my bottom as she pushed me out the door behind Ray and Dad. Something made me think she had a large influence on this outing, even though she did not come with us.

The jagged peaks of the ice packs that stretched along the lake were visible as soon as we passed the Eldorado Mining and Refining factory. Dad had lectured us all the way across town about how dangerous it was to climb the peaks, because they were slippery and slick and he didn't want any accidents. We were to be very careful and stay close to him. The light was starting to set, and the ice fell into angry, dark shadows with the sun flaming behind. I took my Brownie and, lifting it to my eye, snapped some pictures.

"Molly, the first lesson you must learn is never to shoot into the sun. The film will just be overexposed." Dad showed us how to look for "composition" and showed us how light and shadow played on the crevices and ice shards. We walked the whole length of the beach, stopping every few feet to snap a "particularly interesting shape or play of light." I took a whole roll of film.

Returning to our car, Dad told us to wait, and he went back to the beach. I saw him speak to two boys then return to us.

When we got home, a plate of ginger cookies and steaming hot chocolate appeared in quick time. Mom listened as we spilled over with the details of the adventure we had had. The telephone interrupted, and Dad answered. A frown crossed his face and we heard, "I'll be right there." Police stuff, that was for sure.

"A boy has fallen into the lake. He and a friend were playing on the ice jams," he slung back as he rushed out the door.

Ray and I looked at each other, exchanging looks that said it was probably better that we had been prevented from going to the lake without supervision.

As was often the case, when Mom was troubled, she sat down at the piano and picked away at tunes. Ray and I got out the Snakes and Ladders and set it up on the dining room table. Smells from the kitchen told us that supper was in the oven. Flash nuzzled her cold nose against my thigh and Marmalade crawled up on the piano bench beside Mom. Notes from "The Last Rose of Summer" were mixed with Ray's and my chatter.

The sharp jangle of the phone sent Ray dashing to the hallway. "Mom, it's Dad."

Mom returned to the dining room biting her bottom lip. She bent down and gave Ray a big hug then sat at the piano. She struck a dark chord then turned and announced, "They found his body — the boy's. There have been far too many deaths this year, and two of them so young. Your father said it was the same two he told to stay away from the ice jam. He feels responsible and blames himself for not taking them home."

"But they would have just gone back!" Ray exclaimed. "I know those guys; they think they know it all. Nobody could tell them anything."

"You know them?"

"Well, not really, but I know who they are. They go to Central School and are always hanging around the pool hall, smoking and pretending they are tough. Mostly we just ignore them."

"Well, it is very sad, nonetheless. When will youngsters ever learn that grown-ups give them warnings for their own good?"

We knew that Mom was talking to herself. Dad did not make it home for supper and when he finally arrived, he took his plate to his darkroom and shut the door.

Sometime later, we heard him coming up the stairs. He was holding two prints in his hand and was smiling.

"Molly, you broke the rules of photography, but you got amazing shots. Look here."

The photos silhouetted the ice against the sky and the setting sun hung bright in the background. Everyone told me how great my pictures were and suggested I enter them in the photo contest at the library. I did and I won First Prize! Even on sad days, good things can happen.

❊ 18 ❊

SEEING IS BELIEVING

I wandered into an antique store on Walton Street. The wall behind the cash register was a gallery of watercolours showing Port Hope in its early years.

"Port Hope was settled by the United Empire Loyalists, called UEL for short," Miss Weldon explained one day in class. "The history of the town goes back a very long way. As you have probably noticed, the town sits in a three-sided bowl." She cupped her hands to show us how the town looked. "Running east and west is the main street, Walton Street, which is also part of the king's highway across Canada. The centre of the town is settled in a valley like the bottom of a bowl and is sliced through by the Ganaraska River. The ground scoops up toward our school and swings around the valley to end at Lake Ontario. When the town was first settled, the lake provided transportation by ship before there were any roads, and the river provided a source of power for lumber mills. That is what drew the settlers to this town."

Bloomsgrove Avenue was somewhere between east and north of the centre and quite close to Trinity College. There was a lot of "old" money, and majestic homes marched along the waterfront and up Chestnut Hill. Several were dotted through our area, too.

Trinity College was a private school and taught boys who belonged to the Anglicans. They wore dark pants and gray jackets with maroon sweaters and ties. They all looked the same. Mostly they stayed at their school and played rugby and tennis, so we didn't see them very often. Their families lived a long way away from Port Hope, so they slept and ate at the school and never got to go home for lunch. We were not allowed to go on Trinity College School property without permission, but we could see it from the top of College Street.

There was a mystery to that school and the kids who went there. Everyone said they were all rich kids and really lucky to be at such a prestigious school. I thought they were really unlucky to have to stay at the school and not go home to warm bread and peanut butter. Sometimes when Trinity boys walked by our school heading for downtown, the show-off boys in our school would tease them and call them "sissy pants." Sometimes bad words were spoken, and if a teacher or the principal heard them, there was big trouble, and sometimes those boys got the strap. Leo got the strap one day.

I had to go to the office to collect the class reports for Miss Weldon, and I saw Leo pushed in through the door by his teacher — right into the principal's office. The door was open, and I could hear angry words; then I saw the strap come down across Leo's palms. Once, twice, three times — and Leo didn't even cry. Then he came out to sit on the chair beside me. His face was all pinched tight and his hands were red as could be but he didn't cry. Leo sure could get himself into trouble.

"What did you do?" I whispered.

"None of your beeswax," he muttered, rubbing his hands on the thighs of his trousers.

"Did it hurt?" I asked, never having experienced a strapping.

"Nah. The principal's a wimp. Couldn't hit hard enough to hurt a flea!" he snarled back, but I noticed he was blowing on his hands. At the beckoning of his teacher's finger, he rose to follow, shaking his hands in the air.

I could hardly wait to get back to my room to spread the news but as I thought about it walking down the hall, telling everyone would make a hero out of Leo, and being bad enough to get the strap was supposed to be a lesson, not something you were rewarded for. I gave Miss Weldon the report cards and kept my secret about Leo. When I got home, I handed my report card to Mom while relating the story about seeing Leo getting the strap. Mom looked right at me with a strange look on her face — looked as if she was going to say something — but turned away and opened my report card.

"Well done, Molly. We will have to work on your penmanship, though; not good." Her mouth was pursed tight as she moved her head from side to side in a "not-good" way.

"I hate writing!" I struck back. "They make fun of me because I am left-handed and I can't draw the letters as pretty as some."

"There, there, it just takes practice. Consider yourself lucky that you live in these times, because when I went to school the nun took a ruler and smashed it across the thumb of my left hand and broke it. I learned to write right-handed but I still do everything else left-handed."

I stared at my mother in amazement. I couldn't grasp what she had said. "You mean they made you write with your right hand even though you were left-handed?"

"That's right. In fact, the nuns tied our left hands behind our backs so we couldn't use them when it was penmanship lessons. There were two of us in my class. Your grandmother was furious with the nun for breaking my thumb, but I still had to learn to write with my right hand."

When Dad got home that evening, they got into a serious discussion in the kitchen, and enough words drifted into the dining room where I was practising printing f's and F's across lined pages that I figured out it was about Leo's getting the strap. I set my pencil down and crept to the doorway to hear.

"It is totally wrong to try to teach a child right from wrong by using a strap. We should speak to the other parents to see if we can stop this practice."

Dad was nodding and thinking. I knew that he didn't believe in spanking so I guessed he didn't believe in strapping, either. Sometimes I wished he *would* spank us, because his way of punishment was to lecture us on the evils of being bad. When I say lecture, I mean lecture! Ray or I, whichever was on the wrong side of right, had to sit in the chair without moving for what seemed hours while we listened to my father going over and over what behaviour was acceptable. Ray and I often said we knew a smart smack on the bottom would be a whole lot easier than sitting through that torture.

"Let me talk to Ralph," Dad said. Ralph was the principal. "Perhaps we can work out a deal whereby I can give the students a tour of the jail and give them a little indication of what can happen if they continue to do bad things."

"Bill, that is a great idea!" I heard Mom say as she started in my direction. I scurried back to my f's and F's.

And that is how our school got to go to jail. One day a week, a class would walk downtown and see how criminals were treated.

Dad even took them into the courtroom and told them all about sentencing. Miss Weldon thought it was a great thing, and we had a whole week of lessons on behaving. We got to have a mock trial and everything. Billy Meed lost his case and was sent to jail. We dragged four desks into a square and put him in it for the afternoon. He was mighty glad to get out and said even though he was still in the class, it was better to not be selected as a "criminal" and have to be separate from everyone else.

"I hope all of you realize from this exercise that it is no fun paying for your crimes," Miss Weldon said. "Class, we are going to write a letter to Chief Carson to thank him for taking so much time to explain this to the whole school. Molly can take it home today."

I never did tell Miss Weldon about the lectures.

We had lived in Port Hope for nearly a year, and I was almost eight years old, so I was allowed to go downtown by myself to the community hall where the Brownies met. To get there, I passed a large Georgian house set back on Mill Street. You never saw anyone coming or going, just a large, red brick house with commanding white doors standing tall above long cement steps. Patti and I made up stories about the people who lived there. We were sure they were movie stars, just like our cutout dolls of Moira Shearer and Arlene Dahl. We imagined beautiful parties and ladies with flowing gowns and shiny jewels sitting in the parlour smiling at each other and saying nice things. But never could we have imagined what we actually saw.

The winter had vanished and the sun was doing its darnedest to warm up the days. Spring just makes you breathe in that sweet air until your lungs are full to busting. Then you let it all out and fill them again. That's the kind of day it was, and Patti and I were sitting on her back porch doing just that. We decided to play "step on a crack and break your mother's back," a kind of hopscotch without any rules except that you jeopardized your mother's health if you stepped on a crack. The best sidewalk around was in front of the big house, so off we went.

There we were, bouncing up and down on the street, first on one leg then the other, when the front door opened and a woman came out shaking a rug! We froze, hanging in mid-air, I think. That woman shaking the rug was black! Well, all that we could see of her was. She wore a big white apron and a long skirt, but we could see her black face and arms. We just stood staring for all our might. Then we took off running like the devil'd shot us from a cannon for the safety of Patti's back porch.

"That lady was as black as Little Black Sambo," Patti whispered, even though we were a long way away from anyone who could hear us.

"Wherever did she come from?" I whispered back.

After much discussion, we decided that this news was far too important to keep to ourselves, so set off in search of Donna and Becky.

We found them over on Elgin Street with Kate and Diane. Kate and Diane's father, Mr. Denver, was busy in the garden scraping away winter. He was getting the gardens ready to plant. Mr. Denver was very precise and had a stick to measure just how far apart each plant should be placed in a space he had divided off with two boards. His garden had very straight borders, and the flowers I saw last fall always looked perfect. Everyone said so, although sometimes I don't think they meant it as a compliment. His vegetable garden was just the same, tidy and straight. We had a vegetable garden, too, and most times the cucumbers were sprawled across the carrots and climbing up the corn. Not to mention that the peas always fell over and were willy-nilly all over the ground. We got a lot to eat from our garden, though.

As soon as we said our polite "hellos" to Mr. Denver and signalled the girls to get on over to the veranda (the Denvers had a veranda, too), we shared our news. Well, it didn't take any imagination to know that we all high-tailed it back to the big house. I can tell you we stood staring at that house for a donkey's age, and no black person so much as stepped out the door. No matter, we were right back there the next day, but still no "blackie." Right about now, Patti's and my credibility was definitely at stake. We had to go to school the next day, and it was the talk of the play yard. Right after school, a whole gaggle of kids scrambled over to the big house and stood staring at the front door. Now, you have to understand that this was a UEL town, and none of us had ever laid eyes on a black person in all our years, no one in the entire school, even those who were twelve years old! Well, they didn't see one that day, either. Patti and I were in big trouble now.

The next day at recess, it was decided that after school I was going to go up and knock on the door. It seemed to be a great plan until I was about halfway up the walk. My stomach was all funny and I suddenly had to go to the bathroom, but when I turned around everybody was pushing me with the back of their hands and mouthing, "Go — go!" At this point, as I inched forward, I didn't think this was such a good idea. All too soon, I was face to face with the great white door and a brass knocker with a lion's head staring right back at me. *What does one say to a "blackie"?* my head was asking. I decided to use my best manners and claim that we were there to welcome her to the neighbourhood. Now, with a feasible plan, I rapped the knocker three times. Then turned to make a hasty retreat but saw my friends in eager anticipation so turned back to face the lion's foreboding stare. Footsteps approached from the other side. I drew in a big breath and was about to say: "Welcome to the — " when I looked up at the whitest face I had ever seen.

"Yes?" she said very sweetly.

By this time, I had lost every instinct of survival and blurted out, "I thought the 'blackie' would answer the door." Then I stumbled over my words and in recovery added, "I just wanted to welcome her to the neighbourhood."

Looking over my head with intense blue eyes and seeing my friends scurrying away as fast as they could, the lady asked, "Do you live near here, dear?"

Nodding my reply, twisting my skirt into a tight ball, I looked up into an angel's face. She was beautiful. Patti and I were right. A movie star did live here. Gleaming golden hair hung to her shoulders, framing a smiling face that eased my nerves and let me answer.

"I am Molly Carson," I offered.

"Chief Carson's daughter?" she queried. Once again, I nodded. "Hmmm," she hummed. "I think you should come in and have some cookies and we will talk about your visit."

Mrs. Langdon (she introduced herself) led me back to a small sitting room with big windows and a round, glass-topped table with four chairs covered in pale yellow velvet. Tulips and daffodils spilled over a large vase in the centre of the table. Motioning me to sit, she said she would be right back. I couldn't sit; I was way too fidgety. There were so many beautiful things to look at, tiny figurines, pictures of mountains and oceans, and my mother would be really excited to know that there was a large white orchid in the window. I decided to tell Mrs. Langdon that my mother just loved orchids.

I could hear giggling and whispers, and when the door opened, not one, but *two* "blackies" were with Mrs. Langdon. I thought my eyes must be lying.

"Molly, I would like you to meet Daisy and Leila," Mrs. Langdon said very formally.

They were both dressed identically in long skirts and white aprons. Mrs. Langdon explained to them that I wanted to welcome them to the neighbourhood. "But," she said, "I think the real reason is that Molly has never seen a black person before — correct?"

Oh, m'goodness, how did she know? I wanted to die right there on that spot, but cookies and milk were set on the table by four black hands then they reached to shake mine. I stared at their dark skin next to my light, stared at pink skin beneath rounded nails of brown hands and up into shining black eyes.

"Daisy and Leila work for me," Mrs. Langdon explained. "They are sisters and they are from a country called Jamaica."

They sounded funny and said my name so it sounded like "Mauully." They giggled so much it got me going, too.

When I finally got my voice back, I blurted out, "How come your skin is so dark?" My curiosity getting the most of me made me forget all about any politeness that might be required of a visitor.

"Well, I guess we just drank way too much chocolate milk when we was young," they giggled. My mother always told us too much chocolate milk would rot our teeth. Boy, would she ever be surprised to learn that it turned your skin black!

Daisy and Leila stayed in Port Hope for only a few months. They said they missed the island and their family. I could understand that; the boys from Trinity College must feel like that, too. I visited the Langdons' house many times, just to spend time with Daisy and Leila. I was enthralled by their infectious laughter and singsong voices. I learned a lot about Jamaica and at stamp club found some Jamaican stamps for my collection. I was a little disappointed to learn that Mrs. Langdon wasn't a movie star. She was a chemist and her husband was Dr. Langdon, a surgeon at the hospital. Patti never came with me. I think she was afraid to talk to black people. Well, she missed an awful lot of really great cookies!

❋ 19 ❋

MARCH 1945 — SPECIAL OCCASIONS

sat in my car sipping on a frosty milkshake and spied a party of children celebrating a birthday. My thoughts drifted to my first birthday party in Port Hope.

St. Patrick's Day and Easter break were coming, and so was my birthday. Miss Weldon kept us busy colouring shamrocks and green hats to put around the classroom. This was to celebrate St. Patrick's Day, but I was more excited about celebrating my birthday, which fell on Sunday, the 16th, the day before St. Patrick's Day. My very Irish father never failed to mention he would never forgive my mother for not crossing her legs for another day because he wished I'd been born on the 17th. I thought that a very silly thing to say. If I was wishing for something, I crossed my fingers! Miss Weldon asked me if I knew anything Irish to share with the class. I wanted to tell her I could do some Irish dancing, but I didn't have a kilt; so, instead, I offered to sing an Irish song.

"Molly!" shouted Ray. "Would you stop that awful screeching? I am sick to death of Too-ra-loo-ra-loo-ra." But I had to practise. I had to be perfect to sing it for the class so at home I sang it all the time, except when Mom and I were deep in discussions about my birthday party. It was my first-ever party, and I was allowed to invite four friends for cake and games. I knew who I wanted right away: Patti, Donna, Beth, and Lucy. Mom looked at me with that "I'm not so sure" look.

"I am not sure Lucy can come. She is still very fragile. And how will she play games when she is in a wheelchair? Somehow we would have to lift her up the front stairs. She might feel awkward, out of place," explained Mother.

"She is one of my bestest friends! She *has* to come."

Mom and Lucy's mother talked it over, and it was decided that

Lucy would have a rest in the early afternoon, and since it was a Sunday, her father and mine would carry the wheelchair up and down the veranda steps. We played games that Lucy could do, like Snakes and Ladders, Tall Tales, and paper cut-outs, and we ate chocolate frosted birthday cake with gobs of ice cream. I opened gifts from my friends: an *Archie* comic book from Patti, a blue hair barrette from Donna, a red Bakelite bracelet from Beth, and a Bobbsy Twins book from Lucy. When everyone went home, I hugged Mom and told her, "My party — it was the best birthday present ever!"

"Well, Dad and I did get you a gift, and so did Ray."

The two parcels lay on the dining room table and everyone stood grinning as I peeled off the paper from the larger one. Inside was a white blouse with tiny yellow flowers on the collar and a yellow and green plaid skirt. The smaller parcel from Ray had a beautiful, wide, yellow satin ribbon.

"I know it is not a kilt," explained Dad. "But you can tell the class that Irish clans are identified by different plaids. My mother's family's plaid is the McPherson — *this* plaid. My father's family arrived in Ireland many centuries ago from Denmark to fight with King William, so they do not have a plaid." Dad then took me into the living room and showed me some easy dance steps. Soon Mom and Ray joined us. Our house became pure Irish, with Dad whistling an Irish jig and balancing all of his six feet two inches as he jumped up on his toes as light as a fairy.

On Monday morning, my braids were plaited tight as could be and the yellow ribbons stood erect at my scalp. The Polish side of me did not exist that day, and I stood Irish-tall in front of the class, sang the Irish lullaby without missing a note, did a short Irish fling, and explained my heritage plaid. When I was finished, everyone clapped like crazy. Then, led by Miss Weldon, they all sang "Happy Birthday." I was eight years old, Irish, and as happy as could be.

When we came to school the next day, all the St. Patrick's decorations were gone. Miss Weldon handed out new colouring assignments: Easter eggs, and bunnies on which we glued cotton wool to make them all fluffy. Easter was early that year, April 1st, and school was out for two weeks' holidays, starting on Thursday, March 28.

We were all asked to sit quietly in our seats as Miss Weldon had something very important to tell us.

"Class, as you know, my name is *Miss* Weldon. That means I am not married. Well, that is about to change; I am getting married Easter weekend."

The room was choked with silence.

"When class resumes, I will no longer be Miss Weldon. You will have to call me Mrs. Elliott."

Arms jerked high, waving at almost every desk. Miss Weldon gave a little cough and said she would answer all of our questions in turn.

"Is Mr. Elliot handsome?" blurted out Annie.

Miss Weldon's eyes went all smiley and she nodded as she pointed to Richard.

"What does Mr. Elliott do?"

"That's a very good question. He is a fireman. Next." She pointed at me.

"Dave Elliott?" I blurted out and watched her face light up as she nodded. "I know him! He's the greatest! He's the fire *chief*! And he has a firefighter dog, a Dalmatian, Sparky. I know because the fire station is right next to the police station. Are you wearing a white dress?"

Miss Weldon spent time telling us all about Sparky and her wedding dress. She told us that they were going to go to Kingston for a few days after the wedding, and that was a "honeymoon." It was some time before we got back to doing Easter pictures.

Every Easter, my Aunt Nell sent me a new outfit. This year it was a rust-coloured corduroy dress with a scalloped collar and tiny buttons all down the front. A narrow belt at the waist set off the full skirt, and white ankle socks and black patent leather Mary Janes finished the outfit. I didn't have to wait until Easter to wear it, though. The wedding was the day before Easter, and since Dave Elliott was a friend of my dad's, I got to go to the wedding.

"Molly, we didn't tell you that you were going to the wedding because Miss Weldon did not want you to blab it all over the classroom. Not that you are a blatherer or anything like *that*," Mom said with a gentle pinch.

On Saturday morning, a big parcel wrapped in white paper with little silver bells lay on the kitchen table. Mom was rushing about and urging Dad and Ray to hurry. "Bill, we are going to be late. Get a hurry on!" We piled into the car and headed for the United Church. Time was tight, so Dad was "pushing a little hard on the gas," as Mom said. We took the turn at Cavan Street, and Dad swung the wheel hard to round North Street to head up the hill to the church. Beside me on the car seat, the white wrapped gift launched into the air and flew to the floor. Sounds of glass shattering sent looks flying from one to the other.

"Oh dear, the wedding vase got broken," I muttered.

"We will just have to tell them their gift will come later. These things happen," Mom said soothingly to me then with a sharp edge to her voice turned to my Dad, "Bill, slow down, for heaven's sake; just get us there in one piece!"

The wedding was the most beautiful thing I had ever seen. Miss Weldon looked like a fairy princess, dressed all in a white satin gown with a long piece of it trailing along the floor behind her. Mom told me this was called a "train." Why, I will never know — it sure didn't look anything like a train. Dave was waiting at the front looking at Miss Weldon coming toward him. Mom explained in a whisper that he was at the "altar." Dave was grinning from ear to ear, and when Miss Weldon got to him, the man she was walking beside gave her hand to Dave, and they turned to face the altar. The minister talked and talked while I picked at a repaired spot in my stockings until my knees peeped through. Then, right in front of everyone, Dave kissed Miss Weldon! I just couldn't believe what I was seeing. Mom leaned over when I let a sharp intake of breathe escape and told me that Miss Weldon was Mrs. Elliott now, "so it's all right for them to kiss."

The next day was Easter Sunday. The Easter bunny hid candy and little tiny fluffy chicks all over the place. We didn't go to church, but my grandmother and Aunt were to arrive in the afternoon. Aunt Nell and Grandma always brought enormous chocolate eggs from Laura Secord; my aunt brought cream-filled ones, and Grandma brought hollow ones. Mom said we were very spoiled to get such special treats. Grandma brought Ray a big hollow rooster and me a rabbit with candy eyes. I hated the cream-filled ones, so Mom always sliced them into little pieces and picked at them for weeks. We never did tell Aunt Nell about this. "It is better to appear grateful and accept gifts with grace," cautioned Mom. I broke off one piece of my rabbit each day so the yummy treat would last forever. Ray gobbled his rooster all down on Easter day.

In the middle of the Easter break, Mom called me in from skipping on the sidewalk. "We are going to charivari the Elliotts," she announced. "I want you to lie down for an hour because you will be up very late."

"What is a *shivaree*?" I asked.

"It is an old custom. When a bride and groom return from their honeymoon and settle in their own house, a bunch of people wake them up and have a party. The idea is to surprise them, so it is done late at night. It is just for fun and is a way of wishing them a happy life together."

We waited outside across the street from the newly married couple's house for the lights to go out; then, with horns and banging pot lids, we sure caused one big ruckus. There was lots of laughter and yelling. Before you knew it, someone was playing an accordion and someone else had a fiddle. We crowded into Miss Weldon's, now Mrs. Elliott's, living room and sang, ate, and danced until we were worn out. I was the only kid from my class, so I could hardly wait to get back to school to tell my classmates all about getting married.

Before school started again, Ray and I had to clean out the garage. There was still a lot of junk in there from the previous tenants, and we had to get rid of lots of stuff to make room for a new push mower and wheelbarrow. The very first box I went to lift lost its bottom, and a million nails dumped all over the cement floor.

"You better pick up every one of those so Dad doesn't get a flat tire," Ray threatened.

"Please help. I can't ever pick all those up," I pleaded.

"Hey squirt, you spilled them, you pick them up."

"But it was an accident! I need help."

"Tough."

The first fistful I grabbed, I threw right at him then started to run. I stepped on a nail and it went right into my foot. I must have let out one wild scream of pain because Mom was right beside me in no time.

"Oh, dear," she muttered. "This is not good. Molly, the nails are rusty and dirty, so I am going to soak your foot in Epsom Salts; then we will have to go to Dr. Hamilton for a tetanus shot."

"You mean like a needle?" I fretted.

"Yes. This kind of injury is very dangerous if we do not take precautions. You were likely due for a tetanus shot anyway."

I just hated getting a needle but knew that when it had to be, it had to be. Dr. Hamilton told Mom that she was smart to bring me in, "just in case."

"Just in case of what?" I asked

"To prevent tetanus, otherwise known as lockjaw. It is caused by injuries from dirty, rusty things. The disease literally attacks the muscles and nerves and often begins with muscle spasms in the jaw. It can be accompanied by difficulty swallowing and stiffness or pain in the muscles of the neck. It is a nasty business, but fortunately we have an inoculation to prevent it. And, while we are at it, I am going to give you a smallpox vaccination as well. That way you will not have to make another trip."

I left Dr. Hamilton's office feeling like a pincushion, but a stop at Turk's for a caramel fudge ice cream sundae made everything a whole lot better.

Ray had to finish cleaning the garage all by himself, nails and all, and I got to hold an icepack on my sore arm for several days. Ray wasn't any too happy with me, I can tell you, but must have soon forgotten all about it because when the wheelbarrow arrived, he gave me a neat ride, racing halfway up the block and back. I tried to lift the wheelbarrow with Ray in it but only managed to tip it over. There was no way I could manage with him in it, but Dougy could, so Ray did get a ride, too, and so did Dougy. Both Dougy and Ray were getting so tall that their legs hung over almost to the ground, even when they were lying on their backs. Patti arrived and watched expectantly, but the older boys got tired of the wheelbarrow game and shot off on their bikes. Neither Patti nor I were able to lift and steady the barrow, so Patti didn't get a ride.

"It's okay," she said, "my dad gives me a turn lots of times." With that, we wandered off to the front of the house to talk about weddings and movie stars while sitting on the bottom step of the veranda and soaking up the warm March sunshine.

❧ **20** ❧

APRIL 1945

I collected my car and drove up Ontario Street but instead of turning onto Bloomsgrove, I continued toward the art college, where we used to gather on hot summer days. The old building stood as it had those many years ago, but there was a snow fence strung across the lane. I parked the car, stepped over the fence, and wandered past the place where we would all throw our bikes down as we lunged for the cool water of the Ganaraska. Everything was changed; the river had been diverted to help prevent torrents of water racing through the town.

The Ganaraska River travelled into town quietly easing through pasture fields before dropping over a wall of rock at the art college, where it spread out over the shale, leaving behind still, reflective pools in hollowed rocks. Resting only momentarily, it pushed off the rock shelf then gathered momentum as it followed a path between banks of

THE ART COLLEGE

129

willow and twisted roots. It slithered over rounded rocks and slapped the sides of jagged boulders, sending effervescent bubbles dancing in the air. It then wandered at its own pace along its chosen path all the way to the great lake.

The river was a constant, always there but not always gentle or predictable. On warm days, we kids with adventure in our souls would head for the falls in droves. We slid across the shale and sat beneath the tumbling water, letting it wash over us. We lay near the still pools and dragged a wet finger over the dry surface of the rocks to see how quickly the wet streak disappeared. Someone always had a cupped hand full of water ready to toss in another's face or a foot ready to kick up a splash. We ran through the puddles and sunned on the granite shelves. Laughter and chatter rippled across the water.

Serious swimming was done downstream at the file factory, where the river grew deep. Old, abandoned concrete railway supports rose out of the water midstream. They served as diving platforms for swimmers who dared. Ray and I were forbidden to go there, but I knew Ray snuck off and did swim there sometimes.

The file factory commanded the shore along Cavan Street, where a gaggle of frame houses crying for paint used to line up across the road. The only flowers were survivors of another time. Remnants of disembowelled washing machines, bicycle tires, and shells of trucks lay about on the lawns beneath the tilted porches. One house even had an old bathtub and toilet partially hidden under twisted lilac bushes. Dandelions squeezed through cracks in the pavement and boldly took root to nod their golden heads or toss white fluff to the winds. This was the "rough" side of town. But no longer — it, too, had changed, the houses chic, renovated to reflect a new and prosperous time.

Across the river, the land swelled to the northeast, and homes were neatly arranged street by street; order knew its place. This was where Highway 28 came in from the north and joined the town, becoming Ontario Street. A little farther northeast was Trinity College School. That was our side of town.

Hugging Lake Ontario, the landscape rises in majestic cliffs to the west, where stately homes command the view. The river slices the west from the east side of town, flowing southward before it eases toward the Ontario Street Bridge. There it changes direction to head east and snake behind Walton Street before crossing it to change direc-

tion again and once more head south, meandering leisurely through the town park. It leaves the centre of town and forces its way through forests of bulrushes before spilling into the lake, a river no more.

The gentle Ganaraska turned into a demented monster every spring. It broke out of bondage, ripping into jagged icebergs that became missiles that uprooted trees or imbedded them. It sent raging brown foam over its banks depositing all manner of refuse. The water raced for miles, impatient to find the lake. Angry and tormented, it broke free at last, carrying trees torn from the banks, their fresh buds never to leaf, and sent them aimlessly tossing on brown, frothy waves. Shattered tree trunks rammed against banks like daggers plunging for the heart then helplessly split away, dragged once more into the turbulence. The surging water collected assorted planks, upside-down waders, and battered doghouses; anything and everything close to the river's banks were caught up and tossed into the fury. Hurled downstream as if trying to win some race, they rushed away. Frothing and fomenting, the river raged for a few crazed days; then, tired, it became sluggish and just eased over its bed for the rest of the summer.

Spring runoff was awesome, fearsome, and offered its own strange beauty. Townsfolk lined the banks to watch, cameras poised. Curious onlookers crowded the bridges and the shoreline. Messages of its wrath hummed over telephone lines and travelled as fast as the raging river. Stories of other years were shared over many a beer or coffee. That first year in Port Hope, the river raged.

"The river's up!" yelled Dougy as he swung his bicycle into our driveway and eased to a stop. "You have to see this! Come on, let's get on over to Barrett's Bridge."

An unexpected sudden thaw had sent the Ganaraska faster and higher than usual, rushing through the centre of town. The lure was too much for the eight of us, who left our designated safe zone and ventured to Barrett's Bridge. We trudged past terraced homes on our right and the lumberyard on our left.

"I can't hear anything for the roar of the water," Ray yelled into Doug's ear. Doug had left his bike at our house, so we walked over the highway and along Barrett's Street. We could see water on the bridge, sloshing over the roadway, where cars were leaving a wake as they drove over. We could see ice jammed against the shoreline, and the roots of large trees pointing at the sky as they rushed by. The water was up over Cavan Street and its sidewalk, reaching as far as some front doors.

"The logs gave way at Curtis Dam, just north of the town," we heard someone shout.

"This is awesome," claimed Ray, spellbound. Eager to get closer so as not to miss a thing, we felt the spray of the water slapping off the riverbank, and wet earth smells filled our noses. We inched forward, straining to see far up the river.

The northeastern riverbank at Barrett's Bridge stood high before it fell away to the lumber yard, so we were able to venture fairly close, straining to peer over the edge. Water was swirling around the parking lot of the lumber yard. We bent over the edge and stretched our necks to see the white froth foam through the churning water. Leo arrived and shouted loudly, "Let's climb up the trusses and watch the river from the top!" Eager nods surrounded us. "Come on!"

Metal girders rose from the ground on an upward angle then ran straight to the other side of the river before angling to the ground. Most of the kids had climbed the span before, so it was a general consensus they could do it now.

Ray hung back and refused to go along with the idea. That meant I couldn't, either. We stood rooted as our friends, eager for adventure, headed to the bridge. We watched with clenched fists, wishing we had the courage to do what the other six were doing, but we daren't. We had never seen a flooding river before, and to us it was very scary. We watched as our friends gripped the sides of the metal girder and crab-walked to the top. Then they sat down, straddling the metal knee to knee as their lower legs hung over the side. Leo waved in triumph, mouthing that the view was "fearsome."

"Get down from there!" a voice hollered.

We turned to see Mrs. Cross waving frantically at the six kids lined up like starlings on a wire. She lived in one of the terraced homes with high front steps. Eve, her daughter, was running back toward their house.

Patti and Doug lay on their stomachs and eased back down, leading the way for the other four.

"Sissies!" yelled Leo as he stood up turned around and started walking across to the other side. We watched in gripped fascination.

The rest of the kids got off the bridge, but Leo kept going right across the top; then he turned and knelt down to grip the sides to crab-walk down the slope on the other side.

We saw Leo's mouth form "Damn" as he lifted his hand away to release pants cuffs snagged on a piece of sharp metal. One second he was tugging; the next, his legs slid over the side and his hands grasped for a hold that was not there. Everyone reached out as if to catch him, helplessly watching Leo fall backward and downward before he disappeared. He made no sound that could be heard over the raging water. It was as if everything moved in slow motion before sirens split the moment. Ray was holding my arms so tight I had bruises the next day, but right then I didn't even notice.

I saw my dad's police car followed by the fire trucks braking to a stop on the edge of the other bank. People raced to the shore. Arms were pointing at a small figure clutching a tree branch in the rushing water. We huddled, bit our lips, and muttered small prayers for Leo. My mother appeared from nowhere and gathered Ray and me to her, hugging us way too tight.

Firemen raced along the edge of the water waving and pointing. A rubber boat was hurled into the water and we saw it struggle to stay upright before it settled enough for two firemen to step in. A rope was tied to a nearby tree, and the boat dug through the surf. One fireman in the boat reached a grappling hook out into the water, grabbing something. We watched a small, limp body dragged through twisted branches as strong hands reached and heaved it into the dinghy.

"He's dead. He's drowned," I whispered hoarsely, tears tumbling down my nose. In the background I heard Mrs. Cross explain that Eve had called the police. Dad had the desk sergeant notify my mother.

We watched as the boat came ashore, and two firemen kneeled over Leo, doing something to him. Then one fireman lifted and braced Leo against his knee, bending him over, lifting and bending. Mother whispered, "Oh, lucky stars, I think he is breathing." I noticed her fingers were crossed. I did that, too.

My dad picked up the limp shape, strode to his car and drove away. We straggled home very subdued and scared; I mean *scared*! Mother was deathly quiet and when she was quiet we knew it was really, really bad. Ray and I were in really big trouble!

We walked up Ontario Street. Silence hung like thunder. We crossed to Bloomsgrove Avenue and headed home. As we passed the giant willow, we could see my dad planted firmly on the sidewalk, his arms folded across his chest. We knew that stance. The Chief always brought his six feet two inches to full height when authority was needed. I think he found another inch that day.

Thanks to Mrs. Cross's quick thinking and the immediate response of the fire department and police, Leo escaped with a lungful of muddy water, a few scrapes, and a good hiding or the back of his mother's hand laid across the back of his head. My father took Ray and me into the living room and lectured, his Irish brogue punctuating each word in measured clipped tones.

"Do you have any idea how dangerous a flooding river is? Did you for one minute consider that you were doing something very, very stupid? Have you any idea how terrified your mother and I were when we found out you'd gone to the river?" Even though he praised Ray for his decision not to participate, we sat and listened for over an hour to the perils that could have been. Small punishment? Not likely! As was always the case, when my fathered lectured, we were not allowed to move and had to give him our entire attention. I sat with my hands clamped tight between my knees and stared at the carpet the whole time. We thought Leo was lucky getting off with a swift smack across the back of his head.

The river quieted, the town cleaned up and dried off, and life returned to normal. The days became longer, and green shoots pushed through the dank soil. Flash scurried everywhere with her nose raised to any vagrant breeze or stuck it deep into a crevice to root out the earth smells. Her fur danced as she raced from one sniff to another. Patti, Beth, and I sauntered to Donna's house giggling at Flash's funny antics. As we walked past the motorcycle house, we noticed Danny was out polishing his bike. We wandered in just so we could be close to a motorcycle and smell the oil and leather. Flash liked some smells; we liked others.

"How fast does it go?" I asked.

"Aw, not too fast. Just fast enough to get the wind in my hair."

I thought that was kind of a silly thing to say as we watched him swing one leg over the seat, balance the bike, and jump on a lever at the side. He did this a couple of times, then the machine roared to life and Danny swerved out of the driveway waving at us as he left. We watched in reverence.

Donna's mother came out of their house next door with the ever-present tea towel in her hands and asked us if we wanted to see the guppies being born. I must have looked really dumb, because Donna started to laugh at me and tell me that guppies were tropical fish and they had an aquarium upstairs. Her mom had just checked the tank, and the mommy guppy was about to "burst," as she put it. We all scrambled up the stairs and peered into the tank just in time to see lots and lots of teensy weensy baby fish fall out of the bottom of another little fish. They were all bright colours and knew how to swim right away. Donna's mother had another bowl full of water and was scooping up the babies as fast as they popped out. Donna explained that the adult fish ate them if they were not separated. Now, this was the most ridiculous thing I had ever heard — mothers don't eat their babies! At least that is what I thought until I learned about guppies.

When I got home, I told everyone at the dinner table about the guppies and that the babies were going to the pet store because Donna's parents had enough fish.

Ray was looking at Mom with a pleading kind of look but she just shook her head. We were not going to have any guppies. To change the subject, Mom pointed out the window to a woodpecker that was hammering at the metal roof.

"That is how he calls for a mate," Mom explained. "Hopefully they will build their nest close by and we can watch when the babies are hatched."

I asked if the woodpecker mommy would eat her babies and was happy to learn that both woodpecker parents would take very good care of their young.

✻ 21 ✻

STILL APRIL 1945

*S*trolling along Walton Street, I noticed that the clean, elegant, prosperous facades of the chic boutiques that today sell upscale mer-
chandise and antiques were a far cry from the stores that served the
citizens of Port Hope sixty-some-odd years ago.

I loved to go downtown, but permission was given only if one or
more of my friends went with me. "Safety in numbers," Mother
would say. I had no idea what she meant but I just knew I was not allowed to go on my own. It was more fun with a bunch of us, anyway.
Tightly clutching a dime or a quarter, we undertook the serious chore
of deciding what to purchase. That involved scouring the entire main
street.

We would set off skipping along Ontario Street, always stopping at the Pratts' fence to lean over and give Winston, their dog, a
thorough coat-roughing. He was such a hoot, lolloping to the fence
with white fur flying away from his eyes, grey fur bouncing up before
leaping onto the fence with paws bigger than our hands. With his
tongue hanging out of his mouth and eyes dancing, we knew he was
happy to see us. We never failed to reach over and give him big bear
hugs and tell him he was a good boy. He was the woolliest, cuddliest
mutt. Mom told me he was an English sheep dog, not like Flash, who
was a golden cocker. Anyway, when Winston was out, his yard was a
definite stop on our way.

"One foot hop," yelled Patti as we continued our quest. This was
a call to follow her, single file, hopping on one foot for as long as she
could, then switching to the other. "Don't step on a crack or you will
break your mother's back!" was the next command. All the way to
Ontario Street Bridge, we would hop, skip, or sometimes try to do
a cartwheel on a grassy spot until we reached the river. Patti could
do them — cartwheels — I couldn't. One by one, we would mount

the metal guard rails of the bridge, grasping the rail and sidestepping from section to section all the way across, wedging our feet between the bars. Whenever we saw something floating in the water, we would jump back down onto the sidewalk and try to figure out what we were looking at. I spotted something large coming around the bend and we waited for it to get close enough so we could see what it was.

"It's a dead body." "It's a sunken car." "It's an old cow, stiff as a board." Guesses were randomly thrown to the wind. Finally close enough to recognize, a door — a front door — was just riding the current like it knew where it was going! That brought on the giggles as we thought about the house without a front door.

"Well anyone could just walk right in."

"Holy cow, what if you just got out of the bathtub and met them, buck skinny?"

"The old street dogs could just go right in and help themselves to dinner. Or maybe even a skunk!" We imagined ourselves silly.

Standing on the bottom railing, we sidestepped all the way to the hotel. Patti was nervous about the "drunks," so we veered to the other side of the road, then on to Walton Street. There weren't many interesting stores up the hill, so we turned toward the centre of town. We stuck our noses against the window of the drugstore, peering deep before deciding "nothing of interest today." At Christmas, they had a big glass jar with bubbling mothballs that kept us glued to the glass forever. But nothing today. The stationery store was always a "must" stop, and we wandered in to the ever-constant greeting, "Don't you kids go touching anything, now." We headed right for the magazine section and the comic book rack. There were magazines that we were not supposed to see so they were way up at the top of the shelf. We could see most of them had ladies with hardly any clothes on pictured on the front covers. I bent to see what was much more interesting: a new movie stars cutout book with fuzzy fur coats for the lady stars. It was thirty-five cents, and I had only twenty cents. Well, that was that; even if I had been prepared to die to get that book, I just didn't have enough money. So, shrugging my shoulders, off we went to the toy store.

"Hi, girls," Miss Blake welcomed us. She sat high on her stool behind the big wooden counter, always wearing a big welcoming smile that was set off by lots and lots of makeup; she had deep pink painted on her cheeks and a small black dot near her scarlet lips. "Get our allowances today?" she asked in her soft, sweet voice. Politely I nodded and opened my hand to reveal two sweaty dimes. She reached with her bony fingers that glared red at the tips and grasped my hand, closing my fingers over the dimes. "Well, you spend it wisely, dear." Miss Blake always wore movie star clothes with frills and everything. I looked into her shining old eyes and nodded.

The shelves were cluttered with every imaginable kind of toy from model cars and tractors to skipping ropes to windup toys. I don't think dusting was high on Miss Blake's list. We were allowed to play with the windups "only for a few minutes," letting them skittle across the wooden floor. I lingered over the fancy dolls, touching one on the cheek or gingerly touching the fancy dress of another.

"These dolls are so beautiful. I just love them, but I have Janice, so I can't have another. She wouldn't understand." I reasoned, "Besides, I would need to be a millionaire to pay that much." The tag read twenty-five dollars.

Patti and Bev were sorting through the marbles, oohing and aahing over a tiger's eye they spied. Tiger's eyes were supposed to be the luckiest and the best ones to own. Frankly, I liked the ones with different-coloured swirls. I could never figure out how they got those curlicues inside the glass. Bev was holding one from the most expensive box.

"Don't buy it," I said. "The boys will just win it away from you the first game you play and then you will be spitting mad that you lost it."

I spied a tiny pink monkey. I wasn't fond of real monkeys, because one bit me when I was three years old, but this one fit in the palm of my hand and was ever so cute. He was covered in pink, bristly stuff like a teddy bear but wasn't soft. He had a little light brown velvety face and just looked like a little pink monkey man with arms and legs that moved. He could stand up or sit down and he could turn his head! I sat him up on the palm of my hand and when I looked into those shiny black eyes they were looking right at me and I knew he was meant to be mine.

"That's a 'good luck' monkey," Miss Blake announced. "I only got two, and the other one is gone."

"How much?"

"Well, he's forty cents."

Reluctantly, I slowly placed him back on the shelf, turned on my heel, and marched out of the shop with purpose. Patti and Bev were nosing through other stuff as I hollered, "I'll be right back."

Taking care that there were no cars coming down the street, I tore across to the police station and into my dad's office.

Not waiting until he was off the phone, I blurted out, "Dad, you have to give me next week's allowance now!" His big hand came up in a commanding "shush" gesture, so I sank onto a hard wooden chair, folded my arms, and glared at him over his big, messy desk. Finally, he scrawled something on a piece of paper and nodded, hung up the phone, and leaned forward across the desk.

"Well, young lady, why would that be?"

"Miss Blake has the most adorable little pink monkey and he's good luck, she said so, and I just love him and he's the only one left and if I don't get him right now I will be miserable for the rest of my life!"

"Molly, the world is not going to end if you can't have a toy monkey."

"But, Dad, he is 'good luck,' don't you see? I can take him with me when I write spelling tests and do public speaking and all sorts of things, because he will bring me luck. I don't have any 'good luck' thing and Ray has a rabbit's foot on a chain. I need him, I really do." Pausing for breath, I gave my father the most pleading look I could muster.

"Well, now, you get an allowance because you do chores for your mother. You have to earn it. Borrowing on next week's earnings is not a good practice."

Defeated, I slumped lower in the chair, my arms dangling off the armrests. My dad just didn't understand.

"However, I do need a letter delivered to the *Guide* office and I would pay twenty-five cents to someone to run that errand for me."

I was up like a shot, grinning from ear to ear.

"Let me! Let me! I know where the office is. I will run all the way. Please, Dad, please, please, pretty please!"

"Well, one does not get paid until the job is complete; so here," he said, handing me an envelope he licked and sealed. "Off you go."

I don't know how I remembered to be careful crossing the street but I was. Stopping only long enough to stick my head into the toy store, I hollered to Miss Blake that I was coming right back for the monkey. I tore up Walton Street to the *Evening Guide* office, where the local newspaper was printed. Pushing down on the latch and heaving at the door with my hip, I shoved the left side of the big double door open and went up to the counter. I couldn't see anyone even when I stood on tiptoe, so I walked the length of that big black counter and peered around it. No one! There was a little bell on the counter so I banged the little brass button on the top of it and waited. Shifting from foot to foot, the time dragged and I banged the bell again; still no one.

Getting up my courage, I crept to a door at the back of the room where I heard some rumbling noises and pushed it inwards. Clattering and thumping noises roared at me. It was no wonder they hadn't heard that little tinkling bell! An enormous machine with big gears was pulling blank paper off huge rolls and swallowing it. Clutching the letter, with my hands over my ears I let the door slam silently behind me and approached a seated man studiously leaning over a funny-looking board. He was selecting little lead pieces from a box rising at an angle beside him and placing them onto a shallow one in front of him. He would look at a piece of paper, then quick as lightning would grab those little things from one box and set them in the other.

When he saw me, he shouted, "Typesetting — it's how we put the words on the paper."

I moved closer and saw that each little block had a letter on it.

"We put ink on these and put them in the machine, and it prints on the paper going through the machine." I could hardly hear him over the noise but from this vantage point I could see the paper the machine had swallowed coming out the other end and it was a newspaper, full of words. Pointing at the name on the envelope I gave him a querying look. He pointed at a man with a big moustache walking near the big machine. "Be very careful and don't touch anything and stay clear of the press. That printing press can be very dangerous," he shouted.

Having delivered the letter, I pelted out of the office to the quiet of the street. I could hear the thumping in my ears halfway back to the police station, or so it seemed. I raced along Walton Street full-tilt all the way to the bottom and my dad's office. Clutching my newly earned quarter and the two dimes, I smugly entered the toy shop.

"The girls have gone on to the bowling alley, dear, but I have your little monkey in a bag right here."

I held the bag close to my heart as I entered the bowling alley and hopped up on the stool next to Bev at the soda counter. "Cream soda, please," I ordered. I still had a nickel, so the soda tasted really good after my day's work.

I explained to the girls all about going to the *Evening Guide* office and how I earned enough money delivering a very important letter for my dad and that I got paid a "salary" for delivering it and that I bought the monkey. Taking our sodas, we wandered over to watch the bowlers throw balls down the lanes. We cheered when they got a strike and marvelled at how quickly the pin setters jumped up and down to set the pins after a bowler knocked them over. There was an empty lane, so we threw a few balls just to practise — it was allowed.

Patti and Bev had spent their allowances on three marbles each and their soda. We knew we had better get on home so we left the bowling alley and walked over the bridge on Walton (it was cement so we couldn't straddle the rails like the one on Ontario Street). We made sure we stayed on the north side because the tenements beside the river on the south side stank something awful, and there was usually a scruffy-looking type or two leaning against the wall. We turned onto Mill Street. When we reached the intersection of Mill and Ontario, almost all the way home, I realized the most awful thing.

"I left my monkey at the bowling alley! Oh, gosh, what if someone took him?"

All of us hightailed it as fast as our legs would carry us back downtown. When we got to the bowling alley, we checked the soda counter then the benches near the lanes. My heart was hammering with the fear that I had lost my "good luck" forever. A big lump was forming in my throat and I was close to tears. But he really was good luck, because there, sitting on the bench where we had been throwing practice balls, was the little brown paper bag with my pink monkey. I clutched him close to my thumping heart and made up my mind right then and there to call him "Lucky."

Whenever I needed him with me for luck, he travelled in my pocket where I could wrap my fingers around him to feel the luck. The rest of the time, he sat on my dresser looking at his reflection in the mirror.

✳ 22 ✳

MAY 8, 1945

left the main streets and walked toward the park. It was the centre of ceremony and celebration when I was a child, as I expect it still is. Little has changed here, except there is now a parking lot back of John Street where the railway tracks used to be. The old movie house is now a historical attraction, and the beauty parlour is no longer, a trendy bookstore in its place. Somewhere behind me, I hear a bugle sending mournful notes aloft. Long ago, another bugle sounded for those valiant heroes of World War II.

During the long war, everyone was supposed to make sure that no lights shone through their windows at night; some houses covered their windows with dark shutters on the outside, and others had heavy velvet curtains inside. We had dark green roller blinds on all of our windows. If you pulled them too hard they jumped out of the little holder things and tumbled down and landed on you all unrolled. When that happened, it never failed but the wooden roller bopped you on the head. Dad was the only one who could restore the tension just right. A dim light burned in the bathroom all night just in case one of us had to make a quick trip, but other than that, the house was as dark as a sewer hole.

Ray had terror dreams about crocodiles hiding under his bed ready to rear up and eat him and of panting lions lying on the floor waiting to pounce on him. He wanted his light left on but he couldn't, because of the war. Mom used to talk to him for a long time when he went to bed to convince him there were no crocodiles or lions in his room. I had my ever-watchful owl, so I knew nothing could harm me. No owl or anything worked for Ray.

Each night, we checked all the windows in the house, downstairs and up, to make sure the blinds were drawn. When it got dark outside, as long as the blinds were drawn we could use the lights to read or play board games. The big street light just outside my parents' bedroom window never shone while the war raged away on the other side of the world. Dad told us it was so the enemy couldn't see where the towns and cities were located. Now that was silly! I don't know why the enemy couldn't just look at a map. Mommy showed Ray and me where Port Hope was when we were moving. It was right there printed on the map, just a little dot with the words *Port Hope* written right beside it. Lake Ontario was all blue and *all* the towns and cities were on that map! Maybe because they were from Germany, they couldn't read Canadian maps. I know they talked different, not like my dad's Irish accent. They used different words than us, like "*heil*" and "*nein*." Anyway, if they came in the daytime, they would be able see all the houses and factories anyway. You would think grown-ups would know those things.

Mom and Dad most always had their ears turned to the radio. They listened to a station called the BBC. The voices sounded hollow, like an echo — strange, as if they were calling out of a cave. Mother explained that they sounded that way because the broadcast came from Britain across the ocean, by underwater cable, and the an-nouncers had English accents. We had two English war kids in our school, and I knew how they sounded. They had to come to Canada to be safe while Germany bombed their country. They were sad to be away from home but they knew it was for the best. Ellen, in my class, always called Canada "Canadar" and said "sawr" for "saw." She sounded uppity, just like the BBC.

The BBC was always broadcasting war talk and was really bor-ing. I never really paid any mind to all that war stuff. It was more fun playing hopscotch on the sidewalk. Now that the days were warmer and I only had to wear light clothing, and shoes instead of galoshes, it made jumping on the squares a whole lot easier.

One morning as I came down the stairs, I heard the radio playing very loud — the BBC broadcast sounding different, kind of hysterical. I knew what hysterical sounded like because Mom was always telling me not to get hysterical when I was excited and was talking fast and loud. That BBC was for sure "hysterical," just yelling words all over the place. Mom and Dad were all smiles, and Dad was nodding his head and holding Mom really tight and laughing. Before, when they listened to the radio, they always had glum looks on their faces and did not talk, only glanced at each other with sad looks. They would walk away from the broadcast deep inside themselves. But now they made exclamations of "Good boys, take at them!" or "We're moving in — they are on the run." Mom phoned her sister and mother long distance!

Then, on May 8, I came downstairs, and Mom was up on a ladder taking down the dark green roller blinds. The house was brighter, happier. "Oh, sweetheart," Mom sang, "the war is over! Hitler was defeated."

Ray came flying down the stairs right behind me, his big feet thumping on every step; nearly bowled me over. He was shaking Mom's ladder and demanding more information. Mom didn't even get mad; she just laughed. The radio was blaring. The BBC man was cheering, and music was loud in the background. He said that people were spilling out into the streets of London, dancing and crying. Of course, I would be crying too, if my mother caught me spilling stuff in the streets!

I don't think I ever saw my mother so happy. She seemed to bounce from here to there, on the phone and out on the veranda waving at neighbours and exclaiming, "Isn't it wonderful?" She polished everything in sight as she flew around, ruffling Flash's coat and hugging me several times. Later, she quietly sat at the piano and played for hours. I think she was thinking about Uncle Davey and him being shot down over Germany. She forgot about dinner, so Ray and I got to make peanut butter and jelly sandwiches without scrimping on either.

The next night, there was a big party. I mean BIG! The T-junction in the centre of town, just up from the movie theater, was jammed with people. The band was there with bugles and drums. People were blowing horns and shouting, hugging each other, and lots of men slapped each other's backs. Hundreds of people milled about being loud, and there were lots of teenage boys letting out shrill whistles. I was a little afraid but excited, too. My father told me it was a very special night, Victory Day; the whole world was going to celebrate. I wondered how the whole world got to Port Hope so quickly, but they sure were there. Nearly everyone had a flashlight.

The mayor called for quiet through a loud hailer, and the noise rumbled to a stop. "Folks, put out all the flashlights," ordered the mayor. Talking disappeared into a quiet murmur, then everyone was silent, waiting. For four years, the town had lived with blackout orders, and here, now, on the blackest of nights, the crowd just stood still and quiet in the pitch black.

A big switch box hanging on a hydro pole up the street from the police station controlled all the street lights on Walton Street. That is where our family was gathered. Dad swung me onto his shoulders, opened the metal box, pointed at the curled lever, and told me to pull. I was to turn on the street lights! I recognized the importance of what I had been asked to do. I faced the box and grabbed the metal loop. It was really stiff. I was afraid I wouldn't be able to budge it, and my dad would be ever so disappointed with me, and there were a lot of people watching. Mustering all my strength, I grabbed it with both hands, clamped my knees tight to my father's ears, squishing his police hat, took a deep breath and gave it a great yank. A sudden burst of light shone on the hundreds of men, women and children all waving and cheering, their smiles brighter than the light. Cheers exploded and the streets were noisy again, bathed in full light. I asked my dad later what would have happened if the switch had not worked, because it hadn't been used for years. He confessed that he and the utility people had done a test run that afternoon.

Everyone started to swarm down Queen Street and moved all the way to the waterfront, where the glow from a great fire sending flames as high as the buildings could be seen from blocks away. More than the utility people had been busy — the firemen had prepared the biggest bonfire ever.

I remember the singing. I knew "She'll Be Comin' Round the Mountain," so I sang as loud as I could, and nobody told me to quiet down. Dad swept me up on his shoulders and I rode all the way to the Crane Manufacturing Company. Mom and Ray kept pace with Dad's long strides, hand-in-hand, swinging their arms to the music. In awe I watched perfect strangers grab Mom and give her a kiss without Dad even caring. Tons of people pressed through the big metal gates heading to the back of the factory, past the toilets and bathtubs piled high in the storage yard that overlooked Lake Ontario. The fire was blazing with big logs, the flames so high that they must have been seen clear across to Rochester, on the other side of the lake. I heard someone yell, "Look! There is a fire at Rochester, too!" The cheers were loud and immediate as everyone waved toward their allies on the United States side.

All night long, people were crying and hugging, dancing and singing. There were big puppet-like things on poles that were thrown into the fire; effigies, Mom called them. Sparklers were handed out to all the children and we swung them in big circles until the sparks stopped. Someone started playing a bugle, really sad and forlorn. Everyone stopped still and it got really quiet. Mom whispered as she wiped away a tear that the bugler was playing "taps" for those who had fallen. I looked everywhere but didn't see anyone lying on the ground. I started to ask who fell, but the party got noisy again with more hugging and singing and dancing stuff. I watched my dad swing my mom around and around.

I don't know how many people pulled my pigtails and announced, "Johnny will be coming home, isn't that great?" I guessed it was. I didn't know who Johnny was, but he sure was missing a great party by not being home. I got to stay up really, really late.

Talk about the end of the war and Hitler's defeat was everywhere for days and weeks. People asked about friends and family, wanting to know if anyone had heard about so-and-so. There was lots of news about retreating Germans and how Hitler was missing. Then they said he was killed in a bunker. I didn't know what a bunker was but I knew it wasn't true. How could it be? Who was going to believe that? I knew he was still living on Bloomsgrove Avenue. I remembered seeing him on Halloween. I just didn't understand why my dad hadn't arrested him. Grown-ups!

A few days later, Uncle Bill came to see us. He was home on leave when the war ended so would not have to return overseas. Again, there was lots of hugging, and Mommy cried and touched him over and over as if he might disappear and she wanted to feel him once more. He was beautiful in his blue air force uniform and had medals and everything. I got to try on his hat with the RCAF crest on it. He called me "Mollikins," too, but somehow I didn't mind *him* saying it. He brought me a special doll from Burma, whatever Burma is. The doll was kind of weird, with very strange clothes, not like the movie star dolls wore or anything like that; she was dressed in a long, plain skirt and had a shawl over her head. Uncle Bill told me it was the way ladies dressed in Burma. Weird!

My grandmother was there, too, and my Aunt Nell. My aunt always brought really neat presents and she wore very fancy clothes. Her coat and hat always matched, and this time she had a colourful peacock feather in her hat. We had a big dinner in the dining room with the fancy dishes and all. Mom insisted that every light in the house be on. Aunt Nell brought a big roast of beef (Mom was always amazed that Aunt Nell managed to find such luxuries), and we had heaps of mashed potatoes with real butter! Aunt Nell brought special cakes and cream puffs from Diana Sweets all the way from Toronto. My grandfather stayed in Toronto, and Grandmother was really quiet like she was alone, even though we were there.

There was hushed talk about my Uncle Dave, who had been killed over Germany. "Mom, they are trying to locate where he went down," Uncle Bill said. He was very sad and held my grandmother close with his arm around her shoulders. "They will let us know when they do. Darn, he almost made it. He went down so close to the end." Everybody shook their heads as if trying to understand. "We can all be proud of Davey. His unit flew dangerous missions that did serious damage to the German factories and helped win this war." Uncle Bill raised his glass of milk and said, "Here's to David Ballantyne Richardson, Gunner First Class!" Tears tumbled down a few cheeks and everyone's lips were forced sideways into tight twisted smiles.

Later, Mom brought out photo albums and we all watched Uncle Davey walking toward the camera, smiling away at us. That is how we would remember him, always.

❧ 23 ❧

MAY 1945

I drove along Ontario Street to Mill, turned on Walton, and headed up the hill to Cavan. It was a day like the ones many years ago when the canning factory worked full-out processing vegetables. I could see us all in our scuffed sneakers, knees black, and the seats of our pants dusty from sitting on the curb waiting in anticipation as we gazed anxiously up Walton Street.

"What's in the package?" I asked as I slumped into a kitchen chair and reached toward a bulky brown paper bundle the size of a shoebox sitting in the centre of the table. "Dulse," Mom tossed back. "Aunt Charlotte sent it from Toronto." Eagerly, I tore away the string and unwrapped a mound of dark purple leaves that did not look unlike chewing tobacco.

Dulse arrived at our house several times a year. It was dried seaweed — purple seaweed. Even though it sounds awful, our family treated it as a special delicacy, especially my father. Dad explained that not only was it a regular treat in the old country (by that he meant Ireland), it was full of vitamins and healthy stuff. I just liked the intense taste of salt when I peeled off a piece and placed it on my tongue and the transition as the dried crispy sheet turned into slippery goo before I swallowed it. There is nothing at all in the whole world that tastes like dulse. That's what I was eating when the hinge on the front screen door squeaked, announcing someone's arrival.

"The peas are in!" yelled Dougy. Dougy was always the one who got interesting news first. This resulted in a flurry of activity as Ray raced down the stairs, and I grabbed another sheaf of dulse and headed after him. We set off on the run, gathering friends along the way. We ran down Bloomsgrove, across Ontario, along Barrett, over the bridge, and up Cavan to Walton to settle ourselves on the curb where Walton met Cavan.

The canning factory on Cavan Street ran twenty-four hours a day during harvest season. It processed many crops — peas, tomatoes, corn — but peas, the first crop of the year, was the irresistible attraction to us kids. This was my first "pea hunt" but I had sure heard lots about it and so was keen to become a part of the ritual.

Hauled to the canning factory by farm wagon, pea vines loaded with plump pods were piled high and trailed over the sides, almost reaching the ground. The horses with their heavy load rumbled ever so slowly down Walton Street hill and turned the sharp corner onto Cavan, then slowed almost to a stop to manoeuvre the turn. We could hear the screech of metal on metal and the "Easy now, boys!" as the farmers, standing erect, hauled on the wagon brake as hard as they could to keep the wagon from smashing into the horses as they struggled down the steep grade and eased around the corner at a crawl.

This was where we lay in ambush. A line of us squatted along the curb ready to leap into action and attack the wagons as they turned the corner. "There's one!" sent shivers down my back as I watched the horses slip-stepping to hold back the push of the loaded wagon. The wheels rumbled over the asphalt, and the farmer, with one hand on the brake and the other holding the reins, was helpless to fend off any shenanigans. Dougy swatted my shoulder and indicated I was to follow the others and hide behind Hubble's corner grocery store. When the wagon slowed to a near stop, we rushed it. Our grubby, thieving hands reached out as we ran beside the wagons grabbing trailing vines loaded with pods of sweet peas. The farmer urged the horses to move faster with a "gee haw!" and "Get gone, you hooligans!" as soon as the wagon rounded the corner, but we had snagged the loot by this time.

Clutching our treasures tight to our chests, we fled to the back of the stores and the maze of fire escapes down the alley. The clang of the steel rang loud as we scrambled up the steps to claim our own spot. The rusty steps were dotted with brightly coloured shorts and T's, blue jeans, vivid plaid shirts, gaily patterned handkerchief halters, worn by small boys and girls in bare feet and sandaled feet, all trailing vines. We tucked into our plundered treasures, ripping open swollen pods and ran our fingers along the inside letting the peas slide into our open mouths. Emptied pods were carelessly tossed to the ground and conversation hummed: "Got five in my pod," "The smallest are the sweetest," "My pod only had one pea!"

The farmers were somewhat tolerant of our shenanigans and dismissed their losses. Of course, we'd had enough peas after two or three wagons so wandered off to find new adventures, taking time to window gaze along Walton Street as we meandered.

Mom opened a small store just above Cavan Street on Walton, so Walton Street became my daytime home ground after school hours while I waited for the store to close. The store featured fine china and antiques. I learned to dust and handle bone china and to keep my arms tucked neatly to my side when in the store. It was fun opening new shipments, like opening presents, and Mom always talked about the patterns and quality of the china. But my interests were more focused on the happenings on the street.

Jean Kennedy became my newest friend. She lived on Walton Street in an apartment above the sports store: Dewey's Sports, owned by Mr. Dewey. There was a door at the side of Dewey's that led to twenty steps. We always counted them off as we went up the narrow stairway to a black door at the top. The first time I went to Jean's house, I was anxious about what lay beyond that black door looming above those dimly lit stairs, but when she opened the door, a large, bright entrance led to spacious rooms and gleaming wood floors. Her apartment owned one of the fire escapes, and we scrambled up that more often than using the front entrance.

Jean was a scrawny kid, as my mother would say, with stringy dull blonde hair that never shone. But she could outrun me and had the biggest smile I ever saw.

"Let's go watch the drunks at the Ganaraska," she suggested in a hushed voice.

Now, I had specific orders to stay away from the Ganaraska Hotel. My dad warned that natives from the reservation hung out there and they nearly always ended up in a brawl, and he sometimes had to use his billy club to set them straight before he hauled them off to the drunk tank. The Ganaraska, known as The Ganny, was just up Ontario Street next to the bridge. It was a large, grey, limestone building with a ground-level covered boardwalk; it had known better days. That's where the drunks hung out, especially on hot days; better to hang around outside than in, I guess. The inside smelled putrid, like spilled beer and stale tobacco. We could smell it wafting out when we walked past. Regardless of the time of day, there was always an assortment of ragged men lazing about, smoking and talking. Large guffaws and crude language spilled out from under the overhang as they wasted the hours away. Mostly they smiled and waved when we walked by but when a pretty girl tried to scurry past without being noticed, even if she was on the other side of the road, wolf whistles pierced the air.

The narrow alley behind Jean's apartment ran beside the river and out to Ontario Street right between the hotel and the Jex & Smith Funeral Home. Jean and I would use that route on the pretext of going to Broadbent's Bakery. As we skipped along the gravel, we could take in the delicious smells of baking bread that changed to Ganny smells as we got closer to Ontario Street. We were crossing our fingers wishing that we might see a dead person being carted into the back of the funeral home. As luck would have it, a black hearse was backed up to the door. We watched a gurney being rolled in through the back door when all of a sudden an arm fell over the side. Fear of the dead and curiosity grabbed us at the same time.

"Oh! What if they bury that person alive! Did you see it move its arm?" whispered Jean.

"Wow, that is real spooky," I answered in equally hushed tones, visualizing arms reaching out of the cemetery plots, grasping for the life they had just left.

Our imaginations were in full gear as we wound our way to Ontario Street. Dead bodies were the only topic until we safely reached the corner. Language we were forbidden to hear jarred us to a halt. A gaggle of men were leaning against the walls and pillars of the hotel. Torn plaid jack-shirts in various shades were tucked into denim overalls, many sporting patches in unseemly places. They all seemed to wear large rubber boots with red soles. The men sucked on cigarettes or just held them between clenched lips, blowing smoke high into the air. A yellow haze hung beneath the rafters. We swiftly got ourselves around the corner. Giggling at the danger of our adventure, leaning into each other whispering and pointing, we were spotted by one of the men.

"Sst! Come here, cuties. Come on and see ol' Sam," slurred a scruffy-chinned pillar leaner. "Come and let old Sam give ya a nickel for a kiss."

Alarmed, we raced away down the street and dashed into the safety of the doorway of Broadbent's Bakery, peering back at the point of our narrow escape. As soon as our hearts stopped racing and we got our breath, we burst into bouts of laughter, giggled some more, made fun of how silly the men looked, mouthed the forbidden words we had heard, and revelled in the danger of even thinking such words. Falling into Broadbent's, we soon turned our attention to the bakery selections. Our pennies bought us each a donut to munch on, and Jean got a bag of jujubes from the candy counter. We headed for the park, still breaking into fits of hysteria about our dangerous foray past the Ganny and the corpse on the gurney.

Cutting across the railway tracks, headed toward the bandshell, we ran into Bev Trump and Elsie Pitts at the Salvation Army hall. They were several years older than us and seemed to get a charge out of picking on younger kids. Bev's curls were matted to her head in the heat, and, even though it was warm weather, she sniffled with a runny nose, and her teeth were slimy yellow. Her faded turquoise blouse and khaki shorts did little to hide the ground-in dirt of her elbows and knees. Elsie, in contrast, wore a tube top; her bare belly and scanty purple shorts would never have met my parents' approval. She was only eleven years old but she was definitely showing nubs of newly sprouted breasts beneath the tube top and she didn't mind letting everyone know they were there. Her lips were scarlet and her eyes were rimmed with black liner.

"Hey, Jean," Bev moved in on us. "Where are you headin'? Hey, how about giving Elsie and me some of that candy?" She grabbed at Jean's bag of jujubes that Jean just managed to keep out of Bev's grasp. They blocked the path and duck stepped to prevent us from passing.

"You stop, Elsie Pitts," ordered Jean. "Or I will tell my mother and she'll tell your mother you were picking on me." Jean's mother was known for defending Jean's rights.

"Yah, well what do we care. Our mother's a *real* mother. Yours ain't. You got *adopted.*"

"No, I didn't."

"Did too."

THE FIRE ESCAPE

"No! I'm *not* adopted. You quit telling lies."

"Jeannie is adopted," chanted Elsie.

By this time, Bev was pushing with the flat of her hand on Jean's chest, stride-stepping her backwards. Jean was starting to cry. Elsie was holding me back with a straight arm.

"Wimp," Bev announced, grabbing Jean's jujubes, then turned on her heel and signalled Elsie to join her. "Adopted, adopted, adopted . . ." wafted back to us as they sauntered off.

"Come on, Jean," I soothed. "Let's go to your house. Your mother will fix them."

Mrs. Kennedy gathered Jean to her ample bosom, hushed her, held a hanky to her nose, told her to blow, and then wiped her face with a damp cloth while offering lots of sympathy.

"Now, what got you so worked up?" she asked softly as she lifted a tray of fresh-baked cookies from the oven. The open window did little to quell the heat, but Mrs. Kennedy always had to be baking.

Her hair was tied back in a kerchief damp with perspiration, and she wiped her face often with her apron. She scooped a generous number of cookies onto a plate, placed it on the table, and turned to the icebox and poured two glasses of cool lemonade, all in a seamless move. Wringing her hands in her already damp apron, she eased her bulk into a chair.

"Bev and Elsie lied. They say I'm adopted," wailed Jean.

"Bill!" Mrs. Kennedy hollered. Bill was Jean's dad and he was in the parlour reading the newspaper. "Bill, you come here. Now!" The urgency in her voice had Jean and me exchanging puzzled glances.

"Now you tell your father what you just told me," Mrs. Kennedy ordered Jean. She did.

Mr. Kennedy eased slowly into the remaining chair, concentrating on rolling the sleeves of his blue denim shirt up above his elbows, his ever-present pipe clamped in his teeth. He took off his black-rimmed glasses, set the pipe in an ashtray, rubbed his eyes, replaced the glasses, and turned to his wife. "I guess this is a good time," he said.

"Jean," Mrs. Kennedy began, "you have to know you are the most loved any child could be. You are very, very special and don't you ever forget it. You see, many years ago, your dad and I learned that we could never make our own babies. We were very sad because we both wanted our own little girl. We found out there was a special place where one could go and get babies that didn't have a mommy or daddy so we decided we would choose our own little girl. We looked and looked, but there was never one good enough to be our very own little girl."

"Then," said Mr. Kennedy. I turned to look into eyes that were moist and seemed to glow softly. "We found you. It was love at first sight. We brought you home, our own precious little girl, and we have loved you every day since."

"You mean, I really *am* adopted?" sniffed Jean.

"Yes," came the immediate response from both parents. "But that makes you even more special."

They talked about how they drove all the way to the big city of Toronto and saw many, many babies. They said how Jean was the most beautiful of them all and how thankful they were every single day that they had been lucky enough to find her and how happy they were that she was their very own. By this time, Jean was beaming and swallowing cookies between grins and hugs.

I left Jean's house and wandered home, mulling the afternoon's events over in my mind. My mother had absolutely no idea what brought on the slammed door and the comment, "I wish I was adopted," before I stomped off to my room.

❊ 24 ❊

JUNE 1945

*T*rinity College School with its gothic architecture is still attended *by students wearing the traditional uniform. I remember taking swimming lessons there.*

The month of June warmed up, and Lucy was finally able to go outside for recess. The janitor built a ramp for her wheelchair and she could go right outside without being carried. She now had rosy cheeks, and her hair was returning to its glossy sheen. She was able to stay at school all day on Fridays because she would have the weekend to rest.

Summer holidays were fast approaching, generating lots of talk about what we would do when school was out. Some kids were visiting relatives far away, some were going to camp, some played baseball, and some were just hanging out.

One recess, Lucy signalled me and asked me to follow her around the corner away from everyone. She grabbed the top of the wheel and gave it a push. Man, she could get that wheelchair going so fast I really had to get a move on to catch up!

"I want to try something," she said. "Hold my chair still." She then reached over and lifted the footrests, placed her feet on the ground, and pushing hard with her arms she raised herself to a standing position. She did this when she was using the bathroom, so I was not surprised. But next she let go of the chair and her face became all twisted, and I saw one leg move forward, then the other. Instinctively I moved the chair forward in time to catch her as she fell back.

"Lucy! You walked! You walked!"

"Now you know what *I* am going to do this summer," she smirked.

Mother insisted that Ray and I learn to swim. My first attempt had been at Scout camp, but now it became something whereby we had to achieve certain "levels." This meant taking Red Cross-approved lessons for two weeks in June. If we were good, we would collect badges to sew on our swimsuits. Trinity College School had an indoor pool and had an arrangement with the town to allow local children to use the pool for lessons. Mom enrolled both Ray and me.

"Will I learn to dive?" I asked.

"Well, smarty-pants, first you have to be able to swim in water over your head," answered Ray with some authority. *He* could.

I sure did not see this as much of a challenge. For sure I would be able to do *that*! The first day, all our mothers walked us kids to Trinity College School so we would learn how to get inside the building and into the pool. We had to enter the grounds along a specific walkway and were not encouraged to wander. In fact we were told, "Don't!"

I had never been in a pool before, so this was indeed an adventure. Walking down the path, I heard the "slap," "pop" of tennis balls and stared with eyes wide at four tall, lanky boys in white Bermuda shorts and white long-sleeved v-neck sweaters trimmed in maroon, dashing and ducking all over the court. Trinity College students were commonplace in our town but they were always in long, grey pants and maroon blazers off campus. This was the first time I knew they had legs the same as us. I just gawked! I felt my arm being tugged as Mom yanked me in the direction we were heading.

We entered a dark archway, went through a heavy wooden door, and continued along a long corridor with grey stone walls and shiny marble floors. Mom spoke to a man seated at a table for a few minutes, then he pointed us down the hallway.

"Who was that?" I asked in a hollow voice that bounced off the stone walls.

"That is Kevin Reid. He is going to be Ray's swimming instructor. Oh, here we are. Ray, you change in here. There is a door at the other end of the change room that goes directly out to the pool. Molly, this is where you change," said Mother as she pushed me into another dressing room. "It also goes out to the pool." Then she left!

The change room was a busy place lined with lockers, benches, and gossipy, chattering girls. Seeing Mabel, a girl from Grade 4, made me feel better. I waved at her as I approached and sat down beside her looking for guidance.

"Get into your bathing suit, keep your towel, and put the rest in a locker. There is a key on a string. Lock the locker and put the key around your neck so you do not lose it." Mabel instructed me well, and, properly attired, with the precious key around my neck, I walked through the other door. My nose smarted with the chemical smell of chlorinated air. A lady wearing a whistle was standing on the other side of the door.

"Name?" she asked.

"Molly. Molly Carson," I replied.

"Swimming level?"

"Don't know." My eyes were riveted on the huge pool full of dark, dark water. Sunlight streamed in through windows high in the walls, creating sun streaks here and there across the surface like the ones shown on religious cards with Jesus rising to heaven. Puddles shone on the surface of the white tiled floor, and the chlorine stung the back of my throat.

"Can you swim?"

"Some."

"Float?"

"Some."

"Tread water?"

"What's that?"

That answer seemed to pinpoint my ability level and determine that I was to move to a group of kids where Timmy Waters stood. Timmy stuck his tongue out at me. He must have been eating licorice, because his tongue was all black. Then the lady who had asked me all the questions came over.

"Hi. I am Elsa. I will be your instructor. We will be working toward getting your Beginner's Badge." I stared at her welcome smile then lowered my gaze to her long, long legs. I didn't want her to see that I was scared to death. I didn't know what treading water meant, and she was going to be really mad at me for that. The next thing I knew, we were strung in a line beside the edge of the pool at the "shallow end," said Elsa.

As instructed, we sat down and dangled our legs over the side, our feet in the water. The water was freezing! Elsa jumped in anyway and water-walked toward Timmy.

"Timmy, I want you to slip into the water. Don't be afraid — I will hold on to you."

Timmy slipped in with a shriek at the cold water and went under. Elsa reached out and pulled him up, bug-eyed, and held him at arms length. "Okay, I want you to stretch out and lie on your tummy. I will hold you, so it's okay," Elsa reassured Timmy. I watched as she held Timmy under his tummy and moved him through the water. Timmy looked stiff as a board. At this point, I was beginning to feel a little superior. I had done this many times with my mother. A redheaded girl beside me was next. She just sat on the deck and refused to budge anywhere near the water. Elsa coaxed but with no success. "Okay, we will come back to you," she said. Then it was my turn. Instantly all my braveness went out of me. I hesitated and looked into Elsa's eyes. They were looking at me expectantly and unflinchingly. I knew I had no choice, so off I went. Just like Timmy, I went right to the bottom! The shallow end was over my head! Elsa lifted me, laid me on the water, and held me up with her hand under my tummy.

"Okay, Molly. Let's see you float."

"No. The water's too deep," I reacted.

"I'm right here. I won't let you sink. It is no different floating in deep water than shallow. Just lie on top and let the water hold you up." Her reassuring tone let me believe her.

I did it! I did it right there in front of the whole class. And what is more, I was the only kid in my group who could float! If only I knew what it meant to tread water . . .

Of course, I did learn and also learned that water was my element. I took to it just like a fish. I never got used to the cold temperatures and when I asked Elsa why it was so cold, she explained that the pool was kept at sixty-eight degrees in order to make "men" out of the Trinity boys. I figured that meant "to make them tough"; well, I could be tough, too! After every lesson, I would leave the pool shivering uncontrollably, wrapped in my towel and smiling through blue lips.

I loved that pool and every minute I spent in it. Before summer arrived, I could swim well enough to dive off the side and jump off the diving board at the deep end. I got my Beginner's Badge, and Mom sewed it on my bathing suit right where my suit ended at my right leg. "That way, you can see it as well as everyone else." I wore that badge with pride.

When the days got hot, Lake Ontario would become our water park. We still weren't allowed to go to the beach alone, partly because we had to walk through another "rough" part of town to get there. Frame houses hugged the street and broken beer bottles lay along the curb. You just knew dangerous people lived in those houses. Factories lined the waterfront and yellow smoke spewed from the smokestacks. The Crane factory made toilets and sinks, and the Eldorado refined uranium.

On the way to the beach was the train station, and that is where we headed one dreary Saturday morning. Dad had on his police uniform, Mom was dressed in her flowered go-to-meeting dress, and Ray and I were more than presentable for a weekend day. The Duke and Duchess of Windsor were travelling from their ranch near Calgary to New Brunswick. They were making what Dad called "whistle stops," and Port Hope was one.

When we got near the station, there was a long line of people walking up the street, and cars lined up as well. People were carrying flags and waving and smiling at each other. I was puzzled because it was not a parade yet the mood of the crowd was the same. Mom and Dad were chattering away about the Duke and Duchess, so I knew something was up. Dad took off to do some police stuff, and Mom arranged us along the platform in front of the station. It seemed everyone was staring off down the tracks, just waiting. After some time, we heard a faint whistle and knew the train was on its way. An excited buzz went through the crowd as we watched the train getting bigger and bigger. I had seen many trains before but never one as shiny as this one! It just gleamed! We all stood there watching as the train went just beyond the station. A man and lady were standing at the back of the train holding onto the railing. They waved and everyone cheered and waved their flags. A conductor ran down the tracks and set some steps out so our mayor could get onto the train and say a few words about how delighted we were to have these people stop in Port Hope. The man spoke then and said how he was pleased to be here; then he and the lady came off the train and onto the platform. They walked along shaking a few hands and then got back on the train. The whistle blew, and away they went. Everyone was clucking away about how fortunate they were to have seen the Duke and Duchess.

I asked where the Duke and Duchess were. When Mom told me that they were the man and lady that waved and walked about, I could not believe it — they didn't wear crowns or capes or royal clothes at all! How could they have been the Duke and Duchess? If that wasn't the biggest disappointment in my life the next thing that happened was.

Aunt Nell was getting married! It was to be a big affair in Toronto, and we were going to go by train. I had seen trains but never ridden on one. I had mixed feelings, unsure if my tummy would revolt or if a train was different than a car and I would be okay. There was a lot of discussion about the wedding, and for the first time I heard my mother and father in a heated argument.

"I will not allow my daughter to take part in a big show-off ceremony. Why can't they just go the justice of the peace, like we did? Besides, this whole affair is being blown way out of proportion," my father snarled.

"But, Bill, Nell wants Molly to be her flower girl. I think it would be a wonderful experience," Mom countered. "I know it is more than we can afford but I only have one sister."

"I'll have none of it. As far as I am concerned she can get married without us." My father really did not like my aunt — this was the real problem.

The arguments went back and forth for several days, and the final outcome was that we saw Mom off on the train and the rest of us stayed home. I sulked the whole time Mom was away because I would never get to be a flower girl. When Mom returned, she brought me a new sundress and sandals. She told me I didn't miss a thing, even though I was sure I had. Conversation between Mom and Dad was strained, and Ray and I kept glancing at each other wondering what was going to happen.

Then one day, Mom announced we had arrived in Port Hope one year ago. We all talked about how much had happened in that time and how Huntsville seemed such a long time ago and far away.

Our school days came to a close, and on the last day I was sent home with an envelope addressed to my mother and father. I knew it was my final report card. I passed! I would return to Grade 3 at Dr. Powers, my school. Port Hope was now my town, its streets my streets, its people my people.

I steered the old Buick toward the 401 Highway and pointed her east. My story may not have all the facts right, and I certainly substituted names, but I do remember that most of these things happened at some time or other while I lived on Bloomsgrove Avenue. Port Hope disappeared in my rear view mirror as I sped away.

ABOUT THE AUTHOR

Molly O'Connor, a resident of North Gower, Ontario, officially re-tired from the corporate world seven years ago but has been swept back into it as VP Public Relations and Community Affairs for Hous-All Systems Corporation.

Always passionate about playing with words, Molly took her re-tirement as an opportunity to write seriously. She describes her work as light and trite, often with a message. She offers workshops on the art of writing "Flash Fiction" and Memoirs in the Ottawa area and in Sedona, Arizona, where she winters. Another of Molly's interests is writing for children. As a mother of four children and grandmother of seven, she wanted to capture the everyday happenings of a child in small-town Ontario in the 1940s. *Wandering Backwards* tells that story. Molly is also the author of *Fourteen Cups*, a collection of short stories published in 2006.

TO ORDER MORE COPIES, CONTACT:

GSPH

General Store Publishing House
499 O'Brien Road, Box 415
Renfrew, Ontario, Canada K7V 4A6
Tel 1-800-465-6072 • Fax 1-613-432-7184
www.gsph.com